GLENCOE MATHEMATICS

Science and Mathematics Lab Manual

For use with
Glencoe Pre-Algebra
Glencoe Algebra 1
Glencoe Algebra 2

Glencoe McGraw-Hill

New York, New York
Columbus, Ohio
Chicago, Illinois
Peoria, Illinois
Woodland Hills, Califor

D1361658

Graphing Calculator Programs

Six of the labs in this booklet are written for use with the Texas Instruments Calculator-Based Laboratory™ (CBL™) System. Graphing calculator programs required for some of these labs can be downloaded from the disk that accompanies the CBL™ System Experiment Workbook or from the TI Web site ftp.ti.com/pub/graph-ti/cbl/programs (select your calculator from the menu and then look for the wb1 file). The TI-83 Plus versions of these programs also appear in the appendix of this booklet.

Glencoe/McGraw-Hill

A Division of The **McGraw·Hill** Companies

Send all inquiries to:
Glencoe/McGraw-Hill
8787 Orion Place
Columbus, OH 43240

ISBN: 0-07-827760-4

Science and Mathematics Lab Manual

3   4   5   6   7   8   9   10   079   11   10   09   08   07   06   05   04

Contents

* E = Earth Science   L = Life Science   P = Physical Science

Teacher's Guide to Using the Science and Mathematics Lab Manual

Overview This booklet contains 30 labs designed to allow students to explore topics in life science, earth science, physical science, biology, and chemistry through a stimulating, yet straightforward approach. In each lab, students use the tools of algebra to analyze data they have collected or to explore concepts in science.

The labs are correlated for use with *Glencoe Pre-Algebra, Glencoe Algebra 1,* and *Glencoe Algebra 2.* Tables on the next two pages summarize which labs are to be used at each level.

Use of Technology Six of the labs in this booklet are written for use with the Texas Instruments Calculator-Based Laboratory™ (CBL™) System. The CBL System allows students to gather data, retrieve it directly into any CBL-compatible graphing calculator, and then analyze the data using the calculator's data modeling and graphing features. The Texas Instruments CBR™ (Calculator-Based Ranger) can also be used.

When to Use the Science and Mathematics Lab Manual These labs are an enrichment to the classroom experience. They act as follow-up activities to lessons rather than introductory activities for mathematical concepts. Some of the labs might be assigned as outside projects while others require in-class time (mostly because of the materials needed for the experiment). The labs also provide an opportunity to team teach with your science colleagues.

Collaborative Teaching You may wish to consult with the science teachers at your school to do these labs cooperatively as students study concepts used in both their mathematics and science classes. Some of the labs require materials that would be common to most science classrooms.

Cooperative Learning Most of the labs recommend that students work in groups. The emphasis of teamwork and designation of duties helps students to work more efficiently in the given time frame.

Lab Structure Each lab contains Teaching Suggestions and Student Worksheets pages.

The Teaching Suggestions pages include objectives, time required, lists of materials needed and preparation instructions, teaching tips, answers, and suggestions for extending the lab, as appropriate.

The Student Worksheets provide all the information needed for students to complete the lab without additional research.

The Student Worksheets have six sections:

- Introduction
- Objectives
- Materials
- Procedure
- Data and Observations
- Analysis

The *Introduction, Objectives,* and *Materials* list prepares students for intent of the lab and what they will be using.

The *Procedure* provides step-by-step instructions for the activity. The *Data and Observations* section includes graphs, charts, and tables to facilitate data collection and recording. This organizational section helps students in assimilating what they are observing as they prepare to analyze the data. The questions in the *Analysis* section require students to make conjectures about what they have observed. Frequently, they may have to use a formula or equation to arrive at the correct conclusions.

Guide to Using the Science and Mathematics Labs with Glencoe Textbooks

The following chart shows the Science and Mathematics Labs that can be used with various chapters of *Glencoe Pre-Algebra*, *Glencoe Algebra 1*, and *Glencoe Algebra 2*.

The chart on the next page lists the 30 labs and their correlation to the Glencoe texts.

Use of Labs Categorized by Textbook Chapter			
Chapter	**Pre-Algebra**	**Algebra 1**	**Algebra 2**
1	**Lab 1** *(pp. 1-4)* Use with Lesson 1-5	**Lab 7** *(pp. 29-32)* Use with Lesson 1-3	**Lab 20** *(pp. 91-96)* Use with Lesson 1-1
2	**Lab 2** *(pp. 5-8)* Use with Lesson 2-1	**Lab 8** *(pp. 33-36)* Use with Lesson 2-1	**Lab 21** *(pp. 97-102)* Use with Lesson 2-5
3	**Lab 9** *(pp. 37-40)* Use with Lesson 3-5	**Lab 9** *(pp. 37-40)* Use with Lesson 3-4	**Lab 14** *(pp. 63-66)* Use with Lesson 30-2
4		**Lab 11** *(pp. 45-50)* Use with Leson 4-3 **Lab 29** *(pp. 139-144)* Use with Lesson 4-6	
5	**Lab 3** *(pp. 9-12)* Use with Lesson 5-3	**Lab 10** *(pp. 41-44)* Use with Lesson 5-2 **Lab 12** *(pp. 51-56)* Use with Lesson 5-7	**Lab 23** *(pp. 109-114)* Use with Lesson 5-1
6	**Lab 18** *(pp. 81-84)* Use with Lesson 6-5		
7		**Lab 14** *(pp. 63-66)* Use with Lesson 7-2	**Lab 16** *(pp. 71-76)* Use with Lesson 7-2
8	**Lab 4** *(pp. 13-18)* Use with Lesson 8-3	**Lab 15** *(pp. 67-70)* Use with Lesson 8-3	**Lab 25** *(pp. 119-122)* Use with Lesson 8-2
9		**Lab 16** *(71-76)* Use with Lesson 9-5	**Lab 26** *(pp. 123-126)* Use with Lesson 9-4
10	**Lab 5** *(pp. 19-24)* Use with Lesson 10-8	**Lab 17** *(p. 77-80)* Use with Lesson 10-6	**Lab 27** *(pp. 127-132)* Use with Lesson 10-5
11		**Lab 19** *(pp. 85-90)* Use with Lesson 11-5	**Lab 28** *(pp. 133-138)* Use with Lesson 11-2
12	**Lab 22** *(pp. 103-108)* Use with Lesson 12-3 **Lab 6** *(pp. 25-28)* Use with Lesson 12-9	**Lab 18** *(pp. 81-84)* Use with Lesson 12-2	**Lab 24** *(pp. 115-118)* Use with Lesson 12-6 **Lab 13** *(pp. 57-62)* use with Lesson 12-9
13		**Lab 22** *(pp. 103-108)* Use with Lesson 13-5	**Lab 9** *(pp. 37-40)* Use with Lesson 13-1
14		**Lab 23** *(pp. 109-114)* Use with Lesson 14-3	**Lab 30** *(pp. 145-148)* Use with Lesson 14-7

Lab	Pages	Pre-Algebra	Algebra 1	Algebra 2
1	1–4	Lesson 1-5		
2	5–8	Lesson 2-1		
3	9–1	Lesson 5-3		
4	13–18	Lesson 8-3		
5	19–24	Lesson 10-3		
6	25–28	Lesson 12-9		
7	29–32		Lesson 1-3	
8	33–36		Lesson 2-1	
9	37–40	Lesson 3-5	Lesson 3-4	Lesson 13-1
10	41–44		Lesson 5-2	
11	45–50		Lesson 4-3	
12	51–56		Lesson 5-7	
13	57–62			Lesson 12-9
14	63–66		Lesson 7-2	Lesson 3-2
15	67–70		Lesson 8-3	
16	71–76		Lesson 9-5	Lesson 7-2
17	77–80		Lesson 10-6	
18	81–84	Lesson 6-5	Lesson 12-2	
19	85–90		Lesson 11-5	
20	91–96			Lesson 1-1
21	97–102			Lesson 2-5
22	103–108	Lesson 12-3	Lesson 13-5	
23	109–114		Lesson 14-3	Lesson 5-1
24	115–118			Lesson 12-6
25	119–122			Lesson 8-2
26	123–126			Lesson 9-4
27	127–132			Lesson 10-5
28	133–138			Lesson 11-2
29	139–144		Lesson 4-6	
30	145–148			Lesson 14-7

LAB 1 Speed and Acceleration
Teaching Suggestions

Objectives
- Determine the average speed of a small toy car.
- Observe deceleration of the car.
- Determine the conditions that affect or do not affect the speed of a moving object.

Recommended Time 30 minutes

Materials
- stack of books
- wood ramp (about 50 cm long)
- masking tape
- stopwatch or watch with a second hand
- meterstick
- pen or pencil
- toy car or ball

Preparation
Have students bring in toy cars or balls. Stopwatches and metersticks might be borrowed from your school's science department.

Teaching the Lab
- Have students work in groups of 3 or 4. Each member should take on a task of recorder, timer, or distance observer.
- Have students find 20 cm on their metersticks to determine how high the stacks of books should be.
- Remind students that an average is the sum of the data divided by the number of data.

Data and Observations See students' work for answers.

Analysis
Sample answers are given.

  9. The car slowed (or decelerated).
 10. friction between the wheels of the car and the floor and the tape on the floor
 11. The graph should indicate that the speed decreased with each distance marker. No, if the car traveled at a constant speed, the graph of speed versus distance would be a horizontal line.
 12. Do the experiment on carpet or on an uphill grade.
 13. Increase the height of the books or do it on a floor that slopes downward.

Further Explorations
If you were designing an experiment, explain how you could get the toy car to travel without accelerating or deceleration.

LAB 1

Speed and Acceleration
Student Worksheet

Introduction

Speed is defined as the distance an object travels per unit time. Speed is often expressed in kilometers per hour (km/h) and meters per second (m/s). The speed of a car is usually expressed in miles per hour (mph). In most cases, moving objects do not travel at a constant speed. The speed of an object usually increases and decreases as the object moves. Therefore, the average speed is used to describe motion. The formula for average speed is:

$$\text{average speed} = \frac{\text{total distance}}{\text{total time}}$$

Acceleration is the rate at which an object's speed increases, and deceleration is the rate at which an object's speed decreases. Acceleration and deceleration are expressed as meters per second per second (m/s^2). When a car is at constant speed, the acceleration and deceleration are zero.

Objectives

- Determine the average speed of a small toy car.
- Observe deceleration of the car.
- Determine the conditions that affect or do not affect the speed of a moving object.

Materials

- stack of books
- wood ramp (about 50 cm long)
- masking tape
- stopwatch or watch with a second hand
- meterstick
- pen or pencil
- toy car or ball

Procedure

Find Average Speed

1. Clear a "runway," preferably not carpeted that is about 6 meters long.

2. Set up a launching ramp using a stack of books (about 20 cm tall), the wood ramp.

3. Use masking tape to label where the ramp touches the floor as 0 meters. Use the meterstick to make labels at 1 meter, 2 meters, 3 meters, 4 meters, 5 meters, and 6 meters from the end of the ramp.

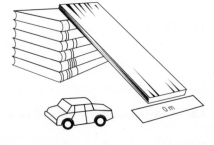

4. Practice releasing the car down the ramp. Observe the car's motion and path. Add or remove books from the ramp so that the car will travel at least 5 meters from the bottom of the ramp.

5. Measure the time the car takes to travel 5 meters. Record the time and distance in Table 1. Calculate the average speed for each trial. Then calculate the average of the speeds.

LAB 1

Speed and Acceleration

Student Worksheet *(continued)*

Measuring Deceleration

6. Release the car down the ramp several more times. Measure the time it takes for the toy car to pass each of the length markers. You may want one team member to record the time as the other two team members call out when the car passes each mark and the time on the clock at those points.

7. Complete four trials and record the times in Table 2. Calculate the average time for each distance. Then calculate the average speed of the car as it passes each marker. Record the result to the nearest 0.1 m/s.

8. Make a graph to compare the average speed of the toy car (*y*-axis) to each marker (*x*-axis) on the next page.

Data and Observations

TABLE 1

Trial	Distance	Time	Average Speed
1	5 m		
2	5 m		
3	5 m		
4	5 m		

Average speed of car = _____ m/s

TABLE 2

	Time(s)				
Trial	1 m	2 m	3 m	4 m	5 m
1					
2					
3					
4					
Average time					

Average Speed (m/s)					

Speed and Acceleration

Student Worksheet (continued)

LAB 1

Graph:

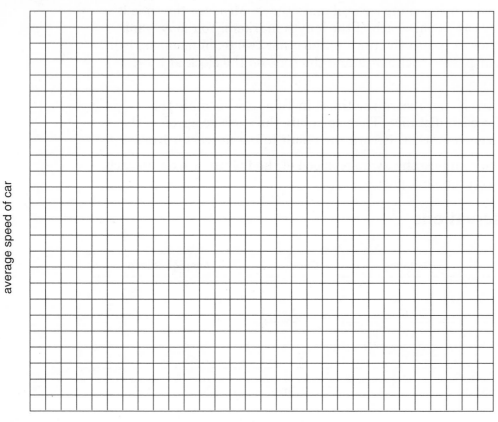

average speed of car

marker distance

Analysis

9. Describe the motion of the car as it moved across the floor.

_____

10. What caused the car to slow down and stop?

_____

11. What patterns do you observe in the graph of the data points? Did the toy car travel at a constant speed? How do you know this?

_____

12. How could you change this experiment to make the toy car decelerate at a faster rate?

_____

13. How could you change this experiment to make the toy car accelerate at a faster rate?

_____

Electrical Charges

Teaching Suggestions

Objectives

- Use friction to produce electrical charges.
- Demonstrate that opposite electrical charges attract while similar electrical charges repel.

Recommended Time

30 minutes

Materials

- 2 balloons
- glass stirring rod
- silk scarf
- string (70 cm long)
- running water

Preparation

Have students bring in balloons, string, and silk scarves. Glass rods might be borrowed from your school's science department. If a sink is not available, you can have students pour water from a gallon jug into another container.

Teaching the Lab

- Have students work in groups of 3 or 4. Each member should take on a task such as recorder or experiment participant.
- Summarize what students are going to be doing in the lab so they will be better prepared to use the time wisely.
- In writing their observations, encourage students to include drawings of what is happening.

Data and Observations

Part A

The balloons repel each other when hanging free.

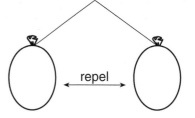

The scarf and the balloon attract each other enabling the balloon to be raised from the floor for a short distance.

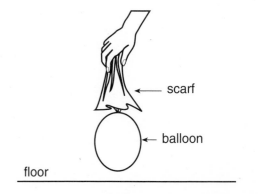

5 *Science and Mathematics Lab Manual*

Part B

The stream of water will appear to bend toward the glass rod, indicating attraction.

Analysis

Sample answers are given.

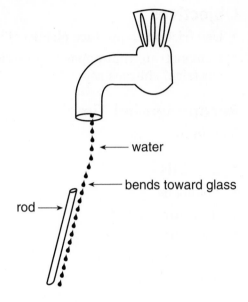

water

bends toward glass

rod

7. negative

8. positive

9. They have similar charges.

10. The balloon has a positive charge and the scarf has a negative charge. Opposite charges attract making the balloon stick to the scarf as the scarf is lifted.

11. positive

12. The stream appeared to bend toward the glass. The normal cause of the bending of the water is the attraction between charged and uncharged objects. Stuents should observe the same results with a negatively charged object.

Further Explorations

There are examples of positive and negative charges easily found at home. Ask students if they have ever walked across a wool carpet in a very dry room and touched a metal surface or another person. What happens? **You sometimes see "sparks."** What are the sparks? **Sparks are static electricity, which is the exchange of ions from one source to another. It might be described as small scale lightning.**

LAB 2

Electrical Charges

Student Worksheet

Introduction

In 1733, a French investigator, DuFay, found that all substances with electrical charges behave either like glass, which DuFay called *positive*, or like hard rubber, which DuFay called *negative*. Rubbing glass and rubber with silk or wool causes the glass to lose electrons and rubber to gain electrons. Bodies with the same charge repel one another, and bodies with opposite charges attract one another. Friction causes the substances rubbed together to gain opposite electrical charges. So, silk or wool may be positive if used to rub hard rubber or negative if used to rub glass.

Objectives

- Use friction to produce electrical charges.
- Demonstrate that opposite electrical charges attract while similar electrical charges repel.

Materials

- 2 balloons
- glass stirring rod
- silk scarf
- string (70 cm long)
- running water

Procedure

Part A

1. Blow up the balloons and tie a balloon to each end of the string.

2. Rub each balloon with the scarf. Hold the string in the center and let the balloons hang free. Record your observations.

3. Cut the string close to one balloon. Rub that balloon with the scarf again and place it on the floor.

4. Let the scarf touch the balloon. Lift the balloon as high as possible. Record your observations.

Part B

5. Turn the water on in the sink to run in a gentle stream.

6. Rub the stirring rod with the scarf. Bring the glass close to the stream of water. Record your observations.

Data and Observations

Part A

What happens when the balloons hang free?

_____

_____

_____

_____

SKETCH:

LAB 2 Electrical Charges

Student Worksheet (continued)

What happens with the balloon on the floor?

_____

_____

_____

_____

_____

SKETCH:

Part B

What happens with the running water and the glass rod?

_____

_____

_____

_____

SKETCH:

Analysis

7. If the scarf gains electrons from the balloons, what kind of electrical charge does the scarf have?

   _____

8. What kind of electrical charge do the balloons have?

   _____

9. Why do the balloons repel each other?

   _____

10. Why can you pick up the balloon with the scarf?

    _____

11. What electrical change did the glass rod have after it was rubbed with the scarf?

    _____

12. What happened to the stream of water when the glass rod was brought close to it? Explain.

    _____

Objectives
- Build a growth chamber for bean seeds.
- Measure and record the height of your plants.
- Prepare a bar graph of your results.

Recommended Time
30 minutes first day, 5 minutes for next 10 days

Materials
- corrugated cardboard
- graph paper
- labels
- metric ruler
- paper towels
- zipper plastic bag
- scissors
- 5 pinto bean seeds per person/group
- stapler

Preparation
Pinto bean seeds should be soaked overnight. Some plastic bags can be written on, eliminating the need for labels.

Teaching the Lab
- Have students work in groups of 2 or 3. After the first day, have team members share the responsibility of taking measurements.
- Make sure students understand how to find the average of a set of data.
- In recording the growth, make sure that students record the actual height day by day and not the increase in height per day.

Data and Observations
Data in the table will vary depending on temperature, moisture, and amount of sunlight.

You may wish to have teams exchange data and graphs. Then have teams evaluate the accuracy of the averages and graphed data.

Analysis
13. roots

14. More growth usually occurs during Days 1–5.

15. usually Day 2

16. Answers will vary. Plants usually do not grow at the same daily rate because of various stages of the growth process and environment factors that change from day to day.

Lab 3

LAB 3

Plant Growth

Student Worksheet

Introduction

Have you ever attempted to measure your change in height from one day to the next? Difficult or almost impossible, isn't it? Plants are ideal for measuring growth changes because a single day may result in 1 or 2 centimeters of change in height.

Objectives

- Build a growth chamber for bean seeds.
- Measure and record the height of your plants.
- Prepare a bar graph of your results.

Materials

- corrugated cardboard
- graph paper
- labels
- metric ruler
- paper towels
- gallon-size zipper plastic bag
- scissors
- 5 pinto bean seeds (soaked overnight)
- stapler

Procedure

Building a Growth Chamber

1. Cut a piece of cardboard that is 10 cm wide and 24 cm long. Fold the cardboard in half. (See Figure 1.)

2. Staple a paper towel to one side of the folded cardboard. (See Figure 2.)

3. Cut a piece of paper towel that is 10 cm long and 4 cm wide. Fold it in half lengthwise and punch 6 small holes near the fold with the point of the scissors. *Use care when using the point of the scissors!* (See Figure 3.)

4. Staple the paper towel strip onto the paper towel already attached to the cardboard near the top. (See Figure 4.)

| **Figure 1** | **Figure 2** | **Figure 3** | **Figure 4** |

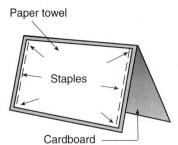

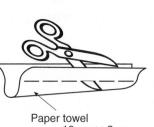

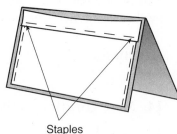

5. Print your name and today's date on a label and attach it to the plastic bag.

6. Stand the folded cardboard inside the plastic bag.

LAB 3 Plant Growth

Student Worksheet (continued)

Recording Plant Growth

7. Place 5 pinto bean seeds into the folded strip of paper towel.

8. Add water to the bottom of the plastic bag and close it. Place the growth chamber near a window.

9. Examine the seeds each day for 10 days. Open the plastic bag and add water as needed.

10. Measure the height of each stem that appears. Record the height in centimeters in Table 1.

11. Total the heights of all 5 plants each day and determine the average stem height. Record this in the last line of Table 1.

12. Use the grid below to prepare a bar graph that will show the average stem height each day (along the *y*-axis) for 10 days (time along the *x*-axis).

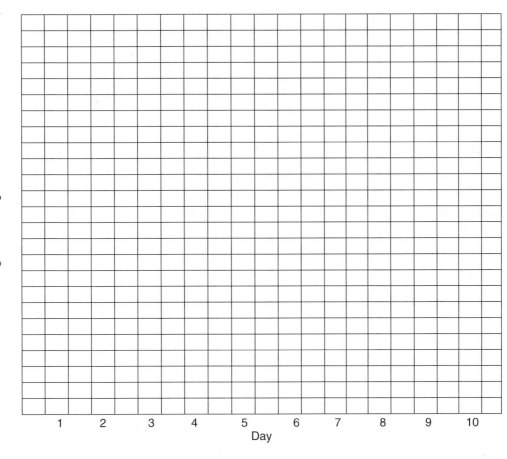

Average Stem Height

Day

Plant Growth

Student Worksheet *(continued)*

Data and Observations

TABLE 1

	DAY									
	1	**2**	**3**	**4**	**5**	**6**	**7**	**8**	**9**	**10**
Seed 1										
Seed 2										
Seed 3										
Seed 4										
Seed 5										
Total										
Average										

Analysis

13. Do roots or stems first appear as the bean seeds grow?

_____

14. Compare the average stem growth during days 1–5 with days 6–10.
When did more growth occur?

_____

15. On what day did stem growth first occur?

_____

16. Did the average stem height increase at a regular rate each day?
Explain.

_____

LAB 4 Graphing Relationships

Teaching Suggestions

Objectives
- Measure the effect of increasing forces on the length of a rubber band.
- Graph the results of the experiment on a coordinate grid.
- Interpret the graph.

Recommended Time
45 minutes

Materials
- several heavy books
- 100-g, 200-g, and 500-g masses
- metric ruler
- 2 plastic-coated wire ties, 10 cm and 30 cm long
- ring clamp
- ring stand
- 3 rubber bands (equal length, different widths)
- colored pencils

Preparation
Acquire gram masses, ring clamp, and ring stand from the science teacher. Have students bring in the three different widths of rubber bands. If you want to consolidate data for a class average, make sure that each group has identical rubber bands.

Teaching the Lab
- Have students work in groups of 3 or 4.
- You may want to suggest that team members work in pairs. While one pair is conducting a part of the trial, another pair can be recording information and graphing. Then the job tasks can switch.

Data and Observations
See student's work for tables and graphs. The data should lie in a fairly linear pattern.

Analysis
Sample answers are given.

14. The graphs describe how much each rubber band stretches as the mass applied increases.

15. It measures the stretchiness or flexibility for the rubber band.

16. The steepness decreases as the widths of the rubber bands increase.

17. The flexibility of a rubber band decreases as its width increases.

Lab 4

18. The length that corresponds to 0 g mass is the original length of the rubber band.

19. Answers will vary. The value will be approximately halfway between 300 g and 500 g values.

20. Suspend the object from the rubber band and measure the length of the stretched rubber band. Use the graph for that rubber band, locate the length, and trace down to find the approximate mass of the unknown object.

Further Explorations

You may want to add another aspect to this experiment. Ask students to make a conjecture as to whether the rubber band returns to its original length after each stretching. Then have them verify their conjectures. They could also make conjectures about how heat and cold affect the stretchiness of a rubber band.

LAB
4

Graphing Relationships
Student Worksheet

Introduction

Most students agree that test grades seem to be related to the amount of time spent studying. If two variables are related, one's value depends on the other's. Test grades are dependent on time studied so test grades would be the dependent variable while time studied represents the independent variable.

Some relationships, when graphed, form a linear pattern. In this experiment, you will investigate how a graph can be used to describe the relationship between the stretch of a rubber band and the force stretching it.

Objectives

- Measure the effect of increasing forces on the length of a rubber band.
- Graph the results of the experiment on a coordinate grid.
- Interpret the graph.

Materials

- several heavy books
- 100-g, 200-g, and 500-g masses
- metric ruler
- 2 plastic-coated wire ties, 10 cm and 30 cm long
- ring clamp
- ring stand
- 3 rubber bands (equal length, different widths)
- colored pencils

Procedure

1. Set up the ring stand, ring clamp, and books as shown.

Trial 1

2. Choose the narrowest rubber band.

3. Securely attach the rubber band to the ring clamp with the 10-cm plastic-coated wire tie.

4. Measure the width of the rubber band. Record this in the table in the Data and Observations section. Measure the length of the rubber band as it hangs from the ring clamp. Record this length as the length value for 0 mass.

5. Attach the 100-g mass to the bottom of the rubber band with the second wire tie. Measure the length of the stretched rubber band. Record this value in the table.

6. Remove the mass and attach the 200-g mass to the bottom of the rubber band. Measure the length of the stretched rubber band. Record this value in the table.

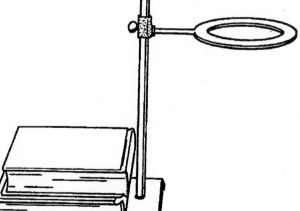

Graphing Relationships

LAB 4

Student Worksheet *(continued)*

7. Remove the 200-g mass from the rubber band. Securely wrap the 100-g and 200-g masses together with the wire ties and attach this to the rubber band. Measure the length of the stretched rubber band and record this value in the table for the 300-g mass.

8. Continue this process of using the various masses to create each mass in the table, measuring the stretched rubber band, and recording the length.

Trial 2

9. Replace the rubber band with a slightly wider one. Make a conjecture about how the stretching of the wider rubber band will differ from that of the narrowest one. Record your conjecture.

10. Repeat steps 3–8 to complete the second column in the table.

Trial 3

11. Replace the rubber band with the widest one. Make a conjecture about how the stretching of this rubber band will differ from the previous two bands. Record your conjecture.

12. Repeat steps 3–8 to complete the third column in the table.

13. Graph the data for all three rubber bands on the same coordinate plane, using a different color pencil for each rubber band.

Data and Observations

Make a conjecture.

For Step 9, how will the stretching of the slightly wider band differ from that of the narrowest one?

_____

_____

_____

For Step 11, how will the stretching of the widest band differ from that of the other two?

_____

_____

_____

_____

_____

_____

Graphing Relationships

Student Worksheet *(continued)*

TABLE	Length of Rubber Band (cm)		
	Trial 1 (narrowest)	Trial 2	Trial 3 (widest)
Mass (g)	_____ mm width	_____ mm width	_____ mm width
0			
100			
200			
300			
500			
600			
700			
800			

Graph

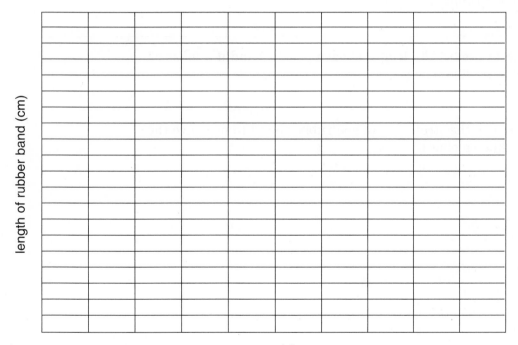

length of rubber band (cm)

mass (g)

Key to colors used in graph:

□ = rubber band _____ mm long

□ = rubber band _____ mm long

□ = rubber band _____ mm long

LAB 4

Graphing Relationships

Student Worksheet *(continued)*

Analysis

14. What information do the graphs portray?

_____

15. What does the steepness of the graph measure?

_____

16. How is the steepness of each of the three graphs related to the width of the rubber band?

_____

17. How is the flexibility of these rubber bands related to their widths?

_____

18. Explain how someone looking at the graph could determine the length of each unstretched rubber band.

_____

19. Use the graph to predict the length of each rubber band if a mass of 400 g is used to stretch it.

_____

20. How could you use the stretching of one rubber band to measure the mass of an unknown object?

_____

Classification by Trait
Teaching Suggestions

Objectives
- Classify geometric shapes.
- Use the words kingdom, phylum, and class in your classification system.
- Determine the characteristics you are using to create you classification categories.

Recommended Time
30-40 minutes

Materials
- shape worksheet
- 2 sheets of paper
- scissors

Preparation
To save time, have students cut out the shapes as homework before doing this activity. This would eliminate the need for sets of scissors.

Teaching the Lab
- Before beginning this lab, engage students in a discussion of some common classification techniques with nonscientific terms. Example: dogs can be divided into different types. Two types might be Labradors and collies. Labradors can include black, chocolate, and yellow. Collies have numerous breeds as divisions of the collie line.
- Have students work in pairs.
- Encourage students to look at the shapes and study their characteristics before beginning the activity. Some patterns in the shapes may become apparent to students immediately.

Data and Observations

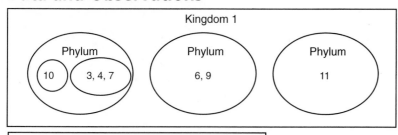

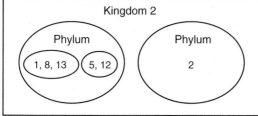

Analysis

9. Members of one kingdom have notches cut out of them and members of the other kingdom do not.

10. Sample answer: notched shapes, non-notched shapes

11. 3, 4, 7, and 10 are formed from circles; 6, 9, and 11 are formed from polygons.

12. 6 and 9 are formed from rectangles; 11 is not formed from a rectangle.

13. Sample answers: notched round shapes (3, 4, 7, 10); notched rectangular shapes (6, 9); notched hexagon shape (11); non-notched polygons (1, 5, 8, 12, 13); non-notched circle (2)

14. single notched round shapes (3, 4, 7); double notched round shapes (10); non-notched rectangular shapes (1, 8, 13); non-notched hexagonal shapes (5, 12)

Further Explorations

Have students make a chart to show the relationships among the different types of polygons.

LAB 5

Classification by Trait

Student Worksheet

Introduction

If you were asked to classify objects, you would probably group things together that have some common characteristics. Scientists have developed a system of classification for living things based on that same principle. Within each larger group, there are subgroups that have even more characteristics in common. Each group and subgroup have been given a name to help simplify the scientists' work.

Objectives

- Classify geometric shapes.
- Use the words *kingdom, phylum,* and *class* in your classification system.
- Determine the characteristics you are using to create you classification categories.

Materials

- shape worksheet
- 2 sheets of paper
- scissors

Procedure

Sorting by Kingdom

1. Cut out the 13 shapes shown on the shape worksheet.

2. Let each piece of paper represent a kingdom. Study the figures and determine what characteristic(s) you could use to separate the 13 figures into two kingdoms. Record those characteristics.

3. Place each figure onto its proper kingdom according to your characteristic(s). Record which figures you have in each of your kingdoms. Let the kingdom with shape 3 be Kingdom 1.

Sorting by Phylum

4. Study the kingdom that contains shape 3. Determine what characteristic(s) you could use to separate the pieces of this kingdom into 3 subgroups called phyla (plural of phylum). Record those characteristics.

5. Record which figures you place in each phylum.

6. Repeat steps 4 and 5 to separate the second kingdom into 2 phyla.

Sorting by Class

7. Study each of your phyla. Determine if any of them can be subdivided into two or more classes.

8. If a phylum can be subdivided into classes, use letters of the alphabet, beginning with A, to categorize each shape in that phylum into a class. Record your classes.

Lab 5

LAB 5

Classification by Trait

Student Worksheet (continued)

Shape Worksheet Cut out each figure. Handle scissors with care.

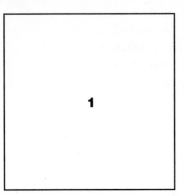

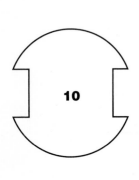

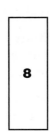

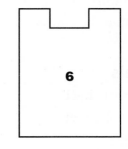

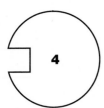

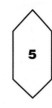

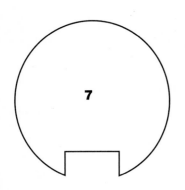

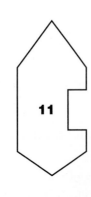

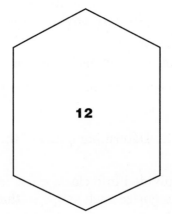

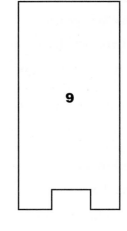

Classification by Trait

Student Worksheet *(continued)*

Data and Observations

Sorting by kingdom

Figures in Kingdom 1: _____

Figures in Kingdom 2: _____

Sorting by phylum

Kingdom 1

Phylum 1	Phylum 2	Phylum 3
characteristic(s):	characteristic(s):	characteristic(s):
shapes:	shapes:	shapes:

Kingdom 2

Phylum 1	Phylum 2
characteristic(s):	characteristic(s):
figures:	figures:

Sorting by class

	Phylum 1	
Kingdom 1	Phylum 2	
	Phylum 3	

Kingdom 2	Phylum 1	
	Phylum 2	

Lab 5

Classification by Trait

Student Worksheet *(continued)*

Analysis

9. How do members of Kingdom 1 differ from Kingdom 2?

_____

10. What two names would you suggest to describe each kingdom? Include *kingdom* in the name.

_____

11. One possibility would be to have shapes 3, 4, 7 and 10 in one phylum. How do these figures differ from shapes 6, 9, or 11?

_____

12. How are 6 and 9 different from 11?

_____

13. If you had to use a name to describe each phylum, what would they be? Include *phylum* in the name.

_____

14. What characteristic(s) did you use to separate the shapes into classes? What would be good names for each? Include *class* in the name.

_____

_____

_____

_____

_____

Predicting Earthquakes

Teaching Suggestions

Objectives

- Make a seismic-risk map of the United States.
- Study the occurrence of earthquakes in the United States.
- Determine which areas are earthquake-prone.

Recommended Time   30 minutes

Materials

- outline map of United States (See p. 28.)
- colored pencils or markers

Preparation   Have students bring colored pencils or markers.

Teaching the Lab

- This activity can be done individually or in small groups.
- Suggest that each member of the group color his/her own map, but the discussion in the Analysis section be done as a consensus of the group.
- Ask students to determine what they think is a damaging earthquake. Would a damaging earthquake in California be of different strength than a damaging earthquake in Ohio? **Yes, because building codes in California require quakeproof construction, whereas those in Ohio would not.**

Data and Observations   See students' maps.

Analysis

5. Alaska, California, Hawaii, Illinois, Missouri, Montana, Nevada, Utah, Washington; all have had 9 or more damaging earthquakes.

6. west of the Rocky Mountains; from California to Alaska

7. There are active faults in the underlying rock layers.

8. While the probability of an earthquake occurring in certain areas is low, every state has had at least one earthquake. It just might not be a damaging one.

9. Scientists can use mappings of earthquake occurrences and severity to predict where another earthquake may be more likely and how severe it might be. However, they cannot predict the exact occurrence of such a quake.

10. The population of Alaska is concentrated in relatively few locations in comparison to the landmass of the entire state. While severe earthquakes may occur, they frequently don't occur in populated areas. Thus, no structural damage is recorded.

LAB 6

Predicting Earthquakes

Student Worksheet

Introduction

There are certain areas of the United States that are earthquake-prone. The risk of disturbances in these areas is great because they lie over active geologic faults, or moving cracks in Earth's crust. While California has the most frequently reported earthquakes, every state in the United States has had at least one earthquake. Seismologists believe that the occurrence of one earthquake indicates another may be possible.

Objectives

- Make a seismic-risk map of the United States.
- Study the occurrence of earthquakes in the United States
- Determine which areas are earthquake-prone.

Materials

- outline map of United States (See page 28.)
- colored pencils or markers

Procedure

1. Choose a color to represent each of the risk zones in the legend of the U.S. map. Color the legend accordingly.

2. Write how many earthquakes and high intensity earthquakes on the map for each state. Enclose the number of high intensity earthquakes in parentheses.

3. Study the data in Table 1. From that information determine your own guidelines for what number of earthquakes qualifies as zone 0, 1, 2, or 3. Record your definitions.

4. Use your color legend to color the map according to the guidelines you defined in step 3.

Data and Observations   (See page 27.)

Analysis

5. In what 10 states have damaging earthquakes occurred the most? Explain your choices.

_____

6. In what section of the United States have damaging earthquakes been concentrated?

_____

7. What does a concentration of damaging earthquakes indicate about the underlying rock structure of the area?

_____

Predicting Earthquakes

Student Worksheet (continued)

8. Sam states that the chance of an earthquake occurring in his hometown is 0%. Is that a reasonable statement? Why?

_____

9. How do you think scientists use seismic occurrence maps to predict the probability of future quakes?

_____

10. Why do you think Alaska, which has more earthquakes than the other 49 states combined, has so few damaging quakes listed in the table?

_____

Data and Observations

TABLE 1

State	Damaging Earthquakes Recorded	State	Damaging Earthquakes Recorded
Alabama	2	Montana	10 (3 high intensity)
Alaska	12 (2 high intensity)	Nebraska	3
Arizona	4	Nevada	12 (3 high intensity)
Arkansas	3	New Hampshire	0
California	over 150 (8 high intensity)	New Jersey	2 (1 high intensity)
Colorado	1	New Mexico	5
Connecticut	2	New York	5 (1 high intensity)
Delaware	0	North Carolina	2
Florida	1	North Dakota	0
Georgia	2	Ohio	6 (1 high intensity)
Hawaii	12 (2 high intensity)	Oklahoma	2
Idaho	4	Oregon	1
Illinois	10	Pennsylvania	1
Indiana	3	Rhode Island	0
Iowa	0	South Carolina	6 (1 high intensity)
Kansas	2	South Dakota	1
Kentucky	5	Tennessee	7
Louisiana	1	Texas	3 (1 high intensity)
Maine	4	Utah	9 (2 high intensity)
Maryland	0	Vermont	0
Massachusetts	4 (1 high intensity)	Virginia	5
Michigan	1	Washington	11 (2 high intensity)
Minnesota	0	West Virginia	1
Mississippi	1	Wisconsin	1
Missouri	9 (2 high intensity)	Wyoming	3

LAB 6 Predicting Earthquakes

Student Worksheet (continued)

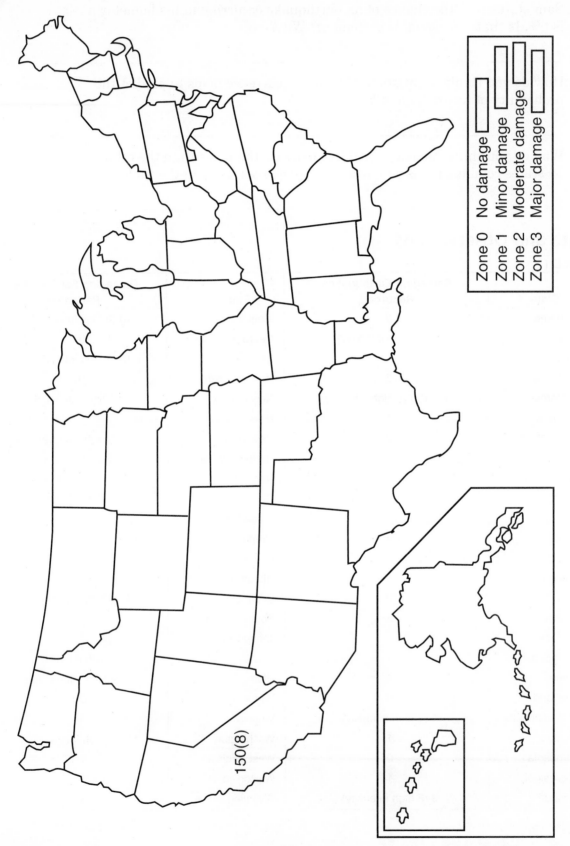

Zone 0 No damage
Zone 1 Minor damage
Zone 2 Moderate damage
Zone 3 Major damage

150(8)

LAB 7 — Using Physical Properties
Teaching Suggestions

Objectives
- Compare the relationships among mass, thickness, and number of pennies.
- Write verbal and algebraic expressions describing how to use measurements of mass and thickness to find the number of pennies in a sample.

Recommended Time
- 1 class period

Materials
- pennies (100)
- balance
- rolls of pennies (10)
- metric ruler

Preparation
Have 10 students each bring in 10 pennies. Ask 10 volunteers to bring in rolls of pennies.

Teaching the Lab
- Have students work in groups of three. Each group member should work with the balance and the metric ruler to take measurements for some of the data.
- Refer students to Figure 1 so they can understand how to measure the thickness of the pennies.
- If necessary, demonstrate how to use the balance to measure a penny.
- If necessary, review how to find a measurement of average thickness and average mass.
- Ask students to consider the thickness of paper in the roll of pennies when measuring thickness. They should subtract thickness for the paper or state that the paper thickness is negligible.

Data and Observations

Number of Coins	Thickness (mm)	Mass (g)
1	1.5	3.1
2	3.0	6.2
3	4.5	9.3
4	5.5	12.4
6	8.5	18.6
8	11.0	24.8
10	14.0	31.0

Using Physical Properties

Teaching Suggestions *(continued)*

Analysis and Conclusions

6. Persons reading the ruler could be inconsistent in judging fractions of millimeters. The surface on which the ruler and the pennies rest could be uneven. Lines on ruler are thick in comparison with measurements.

7. Persons using the scale could be inconsistent in judging measurements. Pennies that have oxidized would have a greater mass than they originally had.

8. Because there could be error in the measurement of a single penny, or because individual pennies could have worn unevenly, using a larger sample will give a better measurement for the average penny.

9. Use the value you came up with for the mass of one penny and divide that into the mass of the pile of pennies to get the number of pennies in the pile.

10. Use the thickness you got for one penny and divide that into the thickness of the stack, or 4.5 cm.

11. Let n = number of pennies.

n = mass of pennies ÷ mass of one penny

12. Let n = number of pennies.

n = 4.5 cm ÷ the thickness of one penny

Further Explorations

Describe how you would estimate the number of nickels remaining in a roll of nickels. Assume you can use the same equipment as you did when measuring the pennies.

LAB 7

Using Physical Properties
Student Worksheet

Introduction

Suppose you've been collecting pennies in a huge milk jug. You're curious to know what your collection is worth, but you don't have the time—or the energy—to count each coin. How can algebra and data about physical properties save you time?

Objectives

- Measure thickness and mass of pennies using a metric ruler and a balance.
- Compare relationships among thickness, mass, and number of pennies.
- Write verbal descriptions and algebraic equations for calculating mass, length, or number of pennies given two other measurements.

Materials

- pennies (10)
- balance
- metric ruler
- roll of pennies

Procedure

A. Measuring Thickness

1. Use the metric ruler to find the thicknesses of 1 penny, 2 pennies, 3 pennies, 4 pennies, 6 pennies, 8 pennies, and 10 pennies. (See Figure 1.) Measure each thickness to the nearest 0.5 mm. Record the thicknesses in the Data Table.

2. Record in the table the number of pennies in the roll. Measure the length of the roll. Record that value in the table.

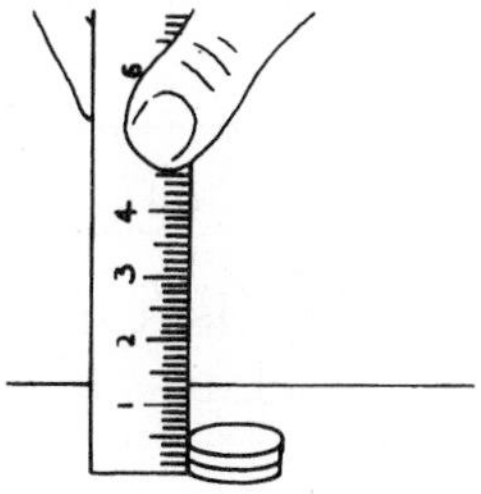

B. Measuring Mass

3. Use the balance to determine the mass of 1 penny, 2 pennies, 3 pennies, 4 pennies, 6 pennies, 8 pennies, and 10 pennies to the nearest 0.1 g. Record the masses in the Data Table.

4. Use the balance to find the mass of the roll of coins. Record the values in the Data Table.

5. Find the average thickness of one penny. Record the value in the Data Table.

Figure 1

Using Physical Properties

Student Worksheet *(continued)*

Data and Observations

Data Table

Number of Pennies	Thickness (mm)	Mass (g)
1		
2		
3		
4		
6		
8		
10		

Average Mass = _____   Average Thickness = _____

Analysis and Conclusions

6. What errors could exist in your measurement of the thickness of the coins?

_____

_____

7. What errors could exist in your measurement of the mass of the coins?

_____

_____

8. Why is it helpful to have more than one measurement for the thickness and the mass of the coins?

_____

9. Write a sentence describing one way that you could use the data about mass to find the number of pennies in a milk jug.

_____

10. Write a sentence describing one way you could use the data about thickness to find the number of pennies in a stack 4.5 cm tall.

_____

11. Write an algebraic equation describing how you would find the number of pennies in a pile that weighs x grams.

_____

12. Write an algebraic equation describing how you would find the number of pennies in a 4.5 cm stack.

_____

pH of Acid Rain

Teaching Suggestions

Objectives
- Use litmus paper to determine if a solution is an acid or a base.
- Use the Texas Instruments Calculator-Based Laboratory System (CBL™) to measure pH.
- Plot pH values on a number line.

Recommended Time
- 2 class periods (Students can practice setting up the CBL™ system in one class period and do the experiment in the next.)

Materials
- solutions in beakers (60)
- red litmus paper (60)
- blue litmus paper (60)
- china markers (10)
- ring stands (10)
- utility clamps (10)
- CBL™ and compatible calculator with a unit-to-unit cable
- Vernier pH probe (PHA-DIN amplifier and 7120B electrode) with CBL DIN adapter (Note: The Vernier CBL pH probe is not included with the CBL unit. Information about purchasing Vernier CBL pH probes is provided on page four of the CBL™ System Experiment Workbook.)

Preparation
- Have students collect rainwater over a week's period or longer to get enough water to test.
- Gather distilled water and tap water. Prepare the vinegar solution using 50 ml vinegar and 200 ml distilled water. Prepare the baking soda solution using one tablespoon of baking soda and 250 ml of distilled water, and prepare the table salt solution using one tablespoon of table salt and 250 ml of distilled water.

Teaching the Lab
- Have students work in groups of three. Each student can test two of the solutions. All of the students should record data on their own charts and number lines.
- If students need help in assembling the CBL™ system, you can refer them to the CBL™ System Guidebook.

Prediction (step 7)
Students should predict that solutions turning red litmus paper blue will have pH values above 7 and solutions turning blue litmus paper red will have pH values below 7.

pH of Acid Rain

Data and Observations

Sample	Acid or Base, or Neutral	pH
Sample 1, Distilled Water		
Sample 2, Tap Water		
Sample 3, Rainwater		
Sample 4, Salt Water		
Sample 5, Vinegar Solution		
Sample 6, Baking Soda Solution		

Analysis

11. Exact points will vary. Points on the number line should agree with values for pH listed in student tables.

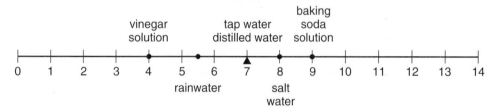

12. Most students will find that the blue litmus paper turned red in a vinegar solution. Some may find the same results for the rainwater.

13. Red litmus paper will turn blue when placed in the salt water and the baking soda solution. Students may not observe a change in either the red or the blue paper when they test distilled water, tap water, and rainwater.

14. Answers will vary but most students will find the vinegar solution and rainwater have pH values that fall to the left of 7, and the distilled water falls right around 7.

15. Answers will vary. Most samples of tap water will fall to the right of 7. The pH of the salt water and baking soda solution falls to the right of 7.

16. Answers will vary according to the pH of rainwater in your area.

Further Explorations

Have students plant grass seed and allow it to germinate using area rainwater. Have them use vinegar to make a solution that has a pH of 5.6 and use that solution to water another sample of grass seed. Have students observe the results.

LAB 8

pH of Acid Rain

Student Worksheet

Introduction

Just how acidic is acid rain? Any solution can be acidic, basic, or neutral. Pure water is neutral and has a pH of 7. Solutions having a pH lower than 7 are acidic and those with a pH above 7 are basic. Acid rain affects aquatic organisms, vascular plants, and earthworms and is an important issue to consider in protecting our environment. Rainwater in your area may not seem acidic if you test it with litmus paper, but if you measure the pH more exactly, you may find that the pH is below 7. By plotting the pH values on a number line, you create a visual comparison of pH values.

Objectives

- Use litmus paper to determine if a solution is an acid or a base.
- Use the Texas Instruments Calculator-Based Laboratory System (CBL™) to measure pH.
- Plot pH values on a number line.

Materials

- solutions in beakers (6)
- red litmus paper (6)
- blue litmus paper (6)
- china marker
- ring stand
- utility clamp
- CBL™ and compatible calculator with unit-to-unit cable
- Vernier pH probe (PHA-DIN amplifier and 7120B electrode) with CBL™ DIN adapter (not included in the CBL unit)

Procedure

A. Acid or Base?

1. Get sample solutions from your teacher. Label your beakers 1 through 6.

2. Pick up a strip of red litmus paper with forceps. Trying not to allow the forceps to touch the liquid, dip the litmus paper into the liquid in sample 1 and remove it. (If the forceps should touch the liquid, wash the forceps in tap water and dry them before using them again.)

3. Use the information in Table 1 to classify each solution as an acid or a base.

4. Discard the litmus paper in a container provided by your teacher. Repeat the process using the blue litmus paper.

5. Record the result of your test in the Data Table.

6. Repeat the testing process for samples 2–6. Use a new piece of litmus paper for each test. Save the solutions in the beakers.

7. Predict which samples are likely to have a pH below 7. _____

_____

Table 1. Litmus Tests

Color Before Test	Color After Test	Type of Solution
Red	Red	Acid or Neutral
	Blue	Base
Blue	Red	Acid
	Blue	Base or Neutral

LAB 8 pH of Acid Rain

Student Worksheet *(continued)*

B. Measuring pH

8. Set up your CBL™ system. Use the unit-to-unit link cable to connect the CBL™ unit to your calculator. Use the I/O ports located on the bottom edge of each unit.

9. Use a utility clamp to attach the pH probe to a ring stand. Place the beaker containing Sample 1 under the probe. Connect the other end of the pH probe to channel 1 (CH1) on the top edge of the CBL™ unit. Turn on the CBL™ unit and the calculator.

10. Download or enter the PH program from the disk accompanying the CBL™ System Experiment Workbook or from the TI Web site. Take a pH reading for Sample 1. Record the pH in the Data Table. Repeat the process for the other five samples. (You do not need to download the PH program again after you have done it the first time.)

Data and Observations

Data Table

Sample	Acid or Base, or Neutral	pH
Sample 1, Distilled Water		
Sample 2, Tap Water		
Sample 3, Rainwater		
Sample 4, Salt Water		
Sample 5, Vinegar Solution		
Sample 6, Baking Soda Solution		

Analysis

11. Plot the measurements for pH on the number line. Label each point on the line with the corresponding sample number.

12. Which samples tested acidic using the litmus paper?

_____

13. Which samples tested basic using the litmus paper?

_____

14. Which samples had pH values that fell to the right of 7 on the number line?

_____

15. Which samples had pH values that fell to the left of 7 on the number line?

_____

16. Scientific studies have shown that a pH value below 5.6 can be harmful to certain groups of living things. Using this information, evaluate the tap water and rainwater in your area. _____

_____

LAB 9

Reflection of Light

Teaching Suggestions

Objectives

- Observe that light travels in straight lines.
- Identify the angles of incidence and reflection of reflected light.
- Find the complements of the angle of incidence and the angle of reflection.
- Describe the relationship between the angle of incidence and the angle of reflection.

Recommended Time

- 1 class period

Materials

- hardcover book (15)
- comb (15)
- flashlight or projector (15)
- masking tape (15)
- pen or pencil (15)
- protractor (15)
- plane mirror (15)
- white paper, 45 sheets

Teaching the Lab

- Have students work in groups of two.

Data and Observations

Observation of light rays in step 2 of the procedure: The light forms straight parallel lines behind the teeth of the comb.

Data Table   Data depend on angles used.

Trial	Angle of incidence	Supplement of the angle of incidence	Complement of the angle of incidence	Angle of reflection	Supplement of the angle of reflection	Complement of the angle of reflection
A	30°	150°	60°	30°	150°	60°
B	41°	139°	49°	41°	139°	49°
C	60°	120°	30°	60°	120°	30°

Teaching Suggestions *(continued)*

Analysis

10. Because the bright areas behind the comb are straight and parallel, the light rays passing between the teeth that form these areas must be traveling in straight and parallel lines.

11. The angle of reflection increased.

12. The angle of incidence equals the angle of reflection for any reflected light ray.

Further Explorations

1. Design an experiment to investigate the reflection of light from a curved mirror. Form a hypothesis relating the angles of incidence and reflection of a light ray reflected from this type of mirror. Test your hypothesis.

2. Investigate the use of plane mirrors in periscopes. Build your own periscope.

LAB 9

Reflection of Light
Student Worksheet

Introduction

Light travels in straight lines called rays. When a light ray strikes a smooth surface, such as polished metal or still water, it is reflected. The angle between the incoming ray and an imaginary perpendicular line that forms a right angle with the reflecting surface is called the angle of incidence. See Figure 1. The angle between the reflected ray and the imaginary perpendicular line is called the angle of reflection.

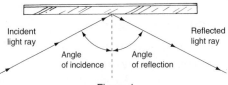

Figure 1

Objectives

- Observe that light travels in straight lines.
- Identify the angles of incidence and reflection of reflected light.
- Find the complements of the angle of incidence and the angle of reflection.
- Describe the relationship between the angle of incidence and the angle of reflection.

Materials

- hardcover book
- comb
- flashlight or projector
- masking tape
- pen or pencil
- protractor
- plane mirror
- white paper, 3 sheets

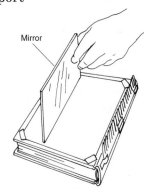

Teeth extend above edge of book.

Figure 2

Procedure

1. Use masking tape to attach one sheet of white paper to the cover of the book. Tape the comb to the edge of the book. The teeth of the comb should extend above the edge of the book as shown in Figure 2.

2. Darken the room. Holding the flashlight as far from the book as possible, shine the flashlight through the comb onto the paper. Support the flashlight on a table or stack of books. Observe the rays of light on the paper. Record your observations in the Data and Observations section.

Mirror

3. Stand the plane mirror at a right angle to the surface of the book cover. Position the mirror at a distance of about two thirds of the width of the book away from the comb. Adjust the mirror so that the light rays hit it at right angles. See Figure 3.

4. Rotate the mirror so that the light rays strike it at various angles of incidence. As you turn the mirror, observe the reflected rays of light.

Figure 3

5. With the mirror turned so the incident rays strike it at an angle of about 30°, study a single incident ray. One partner should hold the mirror while the other traces the path of the ray on the white sheet of paper. Be careful not to change the angle of the mirror while tracing the ray. Label the incident ray *I* and the reflected ray *R*. Draw a line along the edge of the back of the mirror. Label the sheet of paper *Trial A*.

LAB 9

Reflection of Light

Student Worksheet *(continued)*

6. Repeat step 5 using a new sheet of paper on the book. Hold the mirror at a greater angle and trace the ray and the edge of the back of the mirror. Label this sheet *Trial B*. Repeat step 5 for a third time and label the sheet of paper *Trial C*.

7. Use the protractor to draw a dotted line that forms a right angle to the line drawn along the back edge of the mirror. The dotted line should pass through the junction of rays *I* and *R*. See Figure 4.

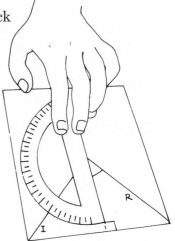

8. Using the protractor, measure the angle of incidence for Trial A. Record this value in the Data Table. Measure the angle of reflection and record this value in the Data Table. Measure and record the angles for Trials B and C in the same way.

9. Find the supplements and complements to the angles of incidence and reflection for Trial A, Trial B, and Trial C. Record the supplements and complements in the Data Table.

Figure 4

Data and Observations

Observation of light rays in step 2 of the procedure:

_____

_____

Data Table

Trial	Angle of incidence	Supplement of the angle of incidence	Complement of the angle of incidence	Angle of reflection	Supplement of the angle of reflection	Complement of the angle of reflection
A						
B						
C						

Analysis

10. Explain how your observations of light passing between the teeth of a comb support the statement that light travels in straight lines.

_____

_____

11. As you increased the angle of incidence, what happened to the angle of reflection?

_____

12. Explain the relationship between the angle of incidence and the angle of reflection.

_____

Variation in the Strength of Electromagnets

Teaching Suggestions

Caution: Students must use care when handling BBs. Any that accidentally fall during the experiment must be immediately retrieved so students do not slip on them.

Objectives
- Construct electromagnets that vary in strength.
- Compare the strength of the magnetic force of four electromagnets.
- Use direct variation and proportion to state the relationship between the strength of the magnetic force and the number of times the wire is coiled around the electromagnet.

Recommended Time
- 1 class period

Materials
- BBs, iron (10 cups of 20 BBs)
- 1.5 V dry cell (10)
- drinking cups (20)
- insulated wire (10)
- iron bolts of the same size, at least 5 cm long (40)
- marking pen (10)
- masking tape (10 rolls)

Preparation
Gather materials.

Teaching the Lab
- Have students work in groups of three.
- Students should wind the wire tightly and evenly around the bolts.
- If necessary, review direct and indirect variations, their equations, and their relation to proportions.
- Instruct students to round their prediction for the number of BBs picked up with 50 coils. Explain that it does not make sense for them to predict that the electromagnet with 50 coils will pick up 23.5 BBs, for example.

Variation in the Strength of Electromagnets

Teaching Suggestions *(continued)*

Data and Observations

Sample Table:

Electromagnet	Number of Turns of Wire	Number of BBs Picked Up	Value of k
A	10	5	$\frac{10}{5} = 2$
B	20	8	$\frac{20}{8} = 2.5$
C	30	13	$\frac{30}{13} = 2.3$
D	40	19	$\frac{40}{19} = 2.1$

Analysis

7. As the number of turns of wire increases, the strength of the magnetic force increases.

8. $y = kx$

9. The values for k should be approximately equivalent and will depend upon the type of bolt used. The value of k for the sample data would be approximately 2.

10. Identical bolts are used so that the value of k remains constant. The size and the material of the bolt affect the strength of the magnetic force.

11. $\dfrac{10 \text{ turns}}{5 \text{ BBs}} = \dfrac{50 \text{ turns}}{x}$

Students' predictions should correspond to their data.

Further Explorations

Have students design an experiment to determine how the strength of the magnetic force of an electromagnet is affected by the amount of current in the coil of the electromagnet. Have them test their predictions and express their results in a direct or indirect variation equation or proportion.

LAB 10 Variation in the Strength of Electromagnets

Student Worksheet

Introduction

A magnetic force exists around any wire that carries an electric current. A wire-wound bolt or nail will become an electromagnet if the wire is connected to a battery or other source of current. The more coils around a bolt or nail, the more the strength of the magnetic force will increase. Using your knowledge about variations, you can make predictions about the strength of an electromagnet.

Objectives

- Construct electromagnets that vary in strength.
- Compare the strength of the magnetic force of four electromagnets.
- Use direct variation and proportion to state the relationship between the strength of the magnetic force and the number of times the wire is coiled around the electromagnet.

Materials

- BBs, iron
- 1.5 V dry cell
- drinking cups (2)
- insulated wire
- iron bolts of the same size, at least 5 cm long (4)
- marking pen
- masking tape

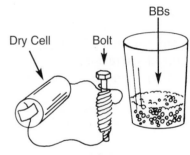

Figure 1

Procedure

1. Place masking tape on the heads of the bolts. Label the bolts A, B, C, and D.

2. Put all the BBs in one cup.

3. Wrap 10 full turns of wire around bolt A. Wrap 20 turns of wire around bolt B, 30 turns around bolt C, and 40 turns around bolt D.

4. Connect the ends of the wires of bolt A to the dry cell as shown in Figure 1. Carefully use your electromagnet to pick up as many BBs as possible. Hold the electromagnet with BBs over the empty cup and disconnect the wire to the dry cell. Make sure all the BBs fall into the cup. Count the number of BBs in the cup. Record this value in the Data Table.

5. Return all the BBs to the first cup.

6. Repeat steps 4 and 5 using bolts B, C, and D.

LAB 10 Variation in the Strength of Electromagnets

Student Worksheet (continued)

Data and Observations

Data Table

Electromagnet	Number of Turns of Wire	Number of BBs Picked Up	Value of *k*
A	10		
B	20		
C	30		
D	40		

Analysis

7. How are both the strength of the magnetic force of an electromagnet and the number of turns of wire in direct variation?

_____

_____

8. If *x* is the number of BBs, *y* is the number of turns of wire, and *k* is the constant of variation, write an equation that shows how the number of turns of wire and the number of BBs are in direct variation.

_____

_____

9. Use the equation to find values of *k* for each of your bolts and record these in the Data Table. What do you notice about the values?

_____

_____

10. Why are identical bolts used in this experiment?

_____

_____

11. Use a proportion to predict how many BBs a bolt wrapped with 50 turns of wire will pick up.

_____

_____

The Relationship Between Density and Concentration

Teaching Suggestions

Objectives

- Determine the densities of ethanol solutions.
- Show the relationship between density and the concentration of aqueous solutions of ethanol.
- Make a graph of your data.
- Use your graph to estimate the concentration of an ethanol solution.

Recommended Time

- 1 class period

Materials

- metric balance (10)
- plastic cups (40)
- plastic microtip pipet (10)
- marking pencil (10)
- ethanol
- grid paper (30 sheets)
- sample ethanol solution, unknown concentration (10)
- distilled water
- aprons (1 per student)
- goggles (1 pair per student)
- gloves (2 per student)

Preparation

- Prepare ten beakers of ethanol solutions with varying concentrations. Students will use these solutions as samples of unknown concentration.

Teaching the Lab

- Students should wear aprons, goggles, and gloves for this lab.
- To assure that students prepare solutions correctly, suggest that they read through the steps of the entire procedure before they begin.

The Relationship Between Density and Concentration

Teaching Suggestions (continued)

Data and Observations

Graphs will vary, but should show a linear relation between density and concentration.

Sample Tables:

Data Table 1

	Liquid			
	Water	Ethanol	50% ethanol solution	Sample solution
Mass of liquid-filled pipet (g)	5.1	4.3	4.7	4.5
Mass of liquid (g)	4.0	3.2	3.6	3.4

Data Table 2

Solution	Concentration	Density (g/mL)
A (0% ethanol: 100% water)	0%	1.00
B (100% ethanol: 0% water)	100%	0.80
C (50% ethanol: 50% water)	50%	0.90
D Sample	unknown	0.85

Analysis

17. The density of water is greater than the density of ethanol.

18. The density of the 50% ethanol solution is lower than the density of pure water and higher than the density of pure ethanol.

19. The pipet that was filled first had the higher concentration of ethanol. The volume of the two pipets is the same, so a lower mass indicates a lower density of ethanol. Lower density indicates a higher concentration of ethanol.

Further Explorations

Have students predict the shape of a graph made by mixing water and glycerin. (The density of glycerin is higher than the density of water.)

LAB 11

The Relationship Between Density and Concentration

Student Worksheet

Introduction

The density of a substance is the mass of that substance in a given volume. What is the relationship between density and concentration? By performing this experiment and graphing your data, you will analyze that relationship. You will also be able to use your graph to estimate the concentration of a solution.

Objectives

- Determine the densities of ethanol solutions.
- Show the relationship between density and the concentration of solutions of ethanol and water.
- Make a graph of your data and use your graph to estimate the concentration of a sample solution.

Materials

- metric balance
- ethanol
- plastic cups (4)
- sample ethanol solution, unknown concentration
- marking pencil
- plastic microtip pipet
- distilled water
- apron
- goggles
- gloves

Procedure

1. Measure the mass of the empty microtip pipet. Record this measurement in the Data and Observations section.

2. Label two of the plastic cups *water* and *ethanol*.

3. Fill the water cup about half full of distilled water. Fill the other cup about half full of ethanol.

4. Squeeze the microtip pipet. Place the tip of the stem into the cup containing water. Draw water into the bulb by releasing the pressure of your hand on the bulb.

5. Hold the bulb with the stem pointing up and the bulb down. Gently squeeze the bulb to expel any air in the pipet. While maintaining pressure on the bulb, insert the stem into the cup of water. Release the pressure on the bulb. The pipet will completely fill with water.

Lab 11

6. Measure the mass of the water-filled pipet. Record this value in Data Table 1.

7. Empty the distilled water in the pipet into the third plastic cup.

8. Repeat steps 4–7 for ethanol, adding the ethanol in the pipet to the water in the third plastic cup.

9. Mix the water and the ethanol in the third cup by gently shaking the cup. Because there are now equal volumes of water and ethanol in the cup, the concentration of the ethanol solution is 50%.

10. Repeat steps 4–6 for the 50% ethanol solution. Discard the solution in the pipet and rinse the pipet.

11. Fill the fourth plastic cup half-full of the sample solution of ethanol. Repeat steps 4–6 for the sample. Discard the solution in the pipet and rinse the pipet.

12. Determine the mass of the water in the water-filled pipet by subtracting the mass of the empty pipet from the mass of the water-filled pipet. Enter this value in Data Table 1.

13. Determine the mass of ethanol and the masses of the two ethanol solutions in the pipet. Record these values in Data Table 1.

14. Determine the volume of the pipet from the mass of the water determined in Step 12. Because the density of water is 1.00 g/mL, the volume of the pipet (expressed in milliliters) is numerically equal to the mass of the water (measured in grams) it holds when it is completely filled. Enter this value as the volume of the pipet.

15. Use the Graph 1 grid to plot the data in Data Table 2. Plot the concentrations of the ethanol solutions on the *x*-axis and the density on the *y*-axis. Label both axes.

16. To use the graph to estimate the concentration of the sample ethanol solution, find the density on the *y*-axis. Determine the concentration by finding the *x*-coordinate for the point on the line of the graph. Record your estimate in Data Table 2.

LAB 11 The Relationship Between Density and Concentration

Student Worksheet (continued)
Data and Observations

Mass of empty pipet: _____ g

Volume of pipet: _____ mL

Data Table 1

	Liquid			
	Water	Ethanol	50% ethanol solution	Sample solution
Mass of liquid-filled pipet (g)				
Mass of liquid (g)				

Data Table 2

Solution	Concentration	Density (g/mL)
A (0% ethanol: 100% water)	0%	1.00
B (100% ethanol: 0% water)	100%	
C (50% ethanol: 50% water)	50%	
D Sample	unknown	

Graph 1

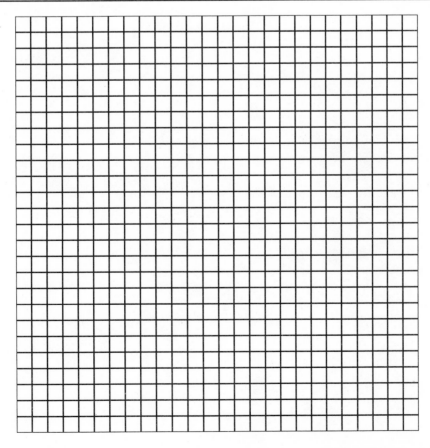

Lab 11

LAB
11

The Relationship Between Density and Concentration

Student Worksheet *(continued)*

Analysis

17. How does the density of water compare with the density of ethanol?

_____

_____

18. How does the density of the 50% ethanol solution compare with the densities of pure water and pure ethanol?

_____

_____

19. Suppose you completely filled two identical pipets with different aqueous solutions of ethanol. The mass of the first filled pipet was less than that of the second. Explain which pipet contained the more concentrated ethanol solution.

_____

_____

_____

_____

LAB 12

Graphing the Efficiency of Solar Collectors

Teaching Suggestions

Caution: Students should use care when punching holes in cans and when using glass.

Objectives

- Build a solar collector and test different cover materials.
- Use the CBL™ to gather and graph data on temperature.
- Determine the line of best fit through a scatter plot of the temperature measures for each material.
- Use data and graphs to evaluate the efficiencies of four cover materials.

Recommended Time

- 2 class periods

Materials

- large coffee can with lid (10)
- small coffee can with lid (20)
- masking tape
- sheet of plastic wrap (10)
- sheet of wax paper (10)
- piece of polyethylene (10)
- pane of glass (10)
- sheet of grid paper (40)
- hammer (3)

- nail (3) (large enough to punch hole for temperature probe)
- newspapers
- paint (flat black)
- paintbrushes (10)
- CBL™
- CBL™ compatible calculator with a unit-to-unit cable
- TI temperature probe
- TI-GRAPH LINK (optional)

Preparation

- Gather materials. Place masking tape around the edges of the pane of glass.
- Prepare a container of paint for each group.

Teaching the Lab

- Have students work in groups of four, with each student doing the procedure for one cover material.
- Students should cover work surfaces before beginning to construct their solar collectors.
- Two students can set up the CBL™ equipment while the other two construct the solar collector.
- Students will want to program their calculators to collect 150 samples (one every 4 seconds).
- Students should not attempt to place the lid around the glass pane.

Lab 12

Graphing the Efficiency of Solar Collectors

Teaching Suggestions (continued)

Data and Observations

Sample Table:

Time (sec)	Temperature (°C)			
	Plastic wrap	Wax paper	Polyethylene	Glass
0	20	20	20	20
20	28	24	26	28
28	30	25	28	30
32	32	26	30	32
36	33	28	31	34
40	34	29	32	36
44	35	30	33	38
48	35	31	33	38
60	35	31	34	39

Sample Hand-Rendered Graph

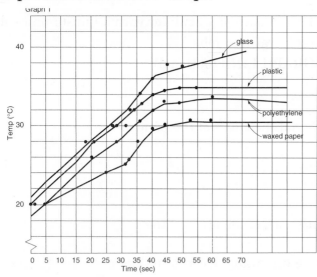

Analysis

16. The glass is the most efficient in collecting heat. The wax paper is the least effective.

17. The lines of best fit should have slopes similar to the stat plot figures shown on the screen.

Further Explorations

Have students use their graphs and data tables to predict what the temperature in each solar collector will be after 15 minutes.

LAB 12 Graphing the Efficiency of Solar Collectors

Student Worksheet

Introduction

With the growing concern about nonrenewable energy sources, the ability to collect and store solar power becomes more and more important. Even though most of the energy that reaches Earth from the sun goes unused, by constructing solar collectors people can harness sunlight—that abundant but elusive resource. In this activity, you will build a simple solar collector. Then you'll use the CBL™ system to measure the heat collected using four different cover materials. You will use your data and graphs to compare the efficiency of the cover materials.

Objectives

- Build a solar collector and test different cover materials.
- Use the CBL™ to gather and graph data on temperature.
- Determine the line of best fit through a scatter plot of the temperature measures for each material.
- Use data and graphs to evaluate the efficiencies of four cover materials.

Materials

- large coffee can with lid (1)
- small coffee can with lid (2)
- sheet of plastic wrap (1)
- sheet of wax paper (1)
- piece of polyethylene (1)
- pane of glass (1)
- sheet of grid paper (1)
- hammer (1)
- nail (large enough to punch hole for temperature probe)
- newspapers
- paint (flat black)
- paintbrush
- CBL™ and compatible calculator with a unit-to-unit cable
- TI temperature probe
- TI-GRAPH LINK (optional)

Lab 12

LAB 12 Graphing the Efficiency of Solar Collectors

Student Worksheet (continued)

Procedure

A. Setting Up the CBL™ Equipment

1. Connect the CBL™ unit to the calculator with the unit-to-unit cable using the I/O ports located on the bottom edge of each unit. Press the cable ends in firmly.

2. Connect the temperature probe to Channel 1 (CH1) on the top edge of the CBL™ unit. Download or enter the TEMP program from the disk accompanying your Experiment Workbook or from the TI Web site.

B. Building the Solar Collector

3. Cover your work surface with newspaper. Paint the inside of the small can black. Let it dry.

4. With a hammer and a nail, punch a hole in one side of the can so the temperature probe can pass through easily. **Caution: Use care when punching the hole in the can.**

5. Cut the center out of the plastic lid of the small can. Leave a 1-centimeter rim around the lid. (See Figure 1.)

6. Stretch the piece of plastic wrap across the top of the small can and put on the lid.

7. Punch a hole in the large can so the temperature probe can pass easily through the hole and into the small can.

8. Shred newspaper and put it in the bottom of the large can.

9. Set the small can on top of the shredded newspaper in the large can. Be sure the holes in the cans align. If the holes don't align, add or remove newspaper until they do.

C. Collecting Solar Power (and Data)

10. Insert the temperature probe as shown in Figure 2. The probe will measure the temperature of the air. Don't have the end of the probe touching the surface of the can. Be sure the CBL™ is turned on and start the program TEMP on the calculator. At the prompt, enter the channel number to which the probe is connected.

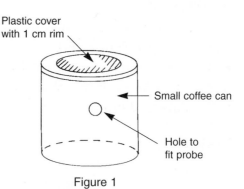

Plastic cover with 1 cm rim

Small coffee can

Hole to fit probe

Figure 1

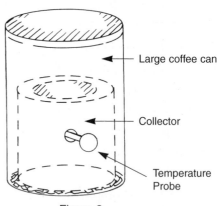

Large coffee can

Collector

Temperature Probe

Figure 2

LAB 12

Graphing the Efficiency of Solar Collectors

Student Worksheet *(continued)*

11. At the prompt, enter the number of samples that you want to take in a ten-minute time period. A sample should be taken every four seconds. When ready, place the cans in the sun and immediately press ENTER on your calculator to start collecting data. Record some of your measurements of the temperatures in the Data Table. You don't need to record every measurement the CBL™ takes.

12. When all samples are taken, a STAT PLOT of time (seconds) versus temperature (°C) will be displayed. Press TRACE on the STAT PLOT to find the initial and final temperature values. Save the temperature in L4 and the time data in L5 to a computer using the TI-GRAPH LINK. Record these measurements in the Data Table.

13. Repeat steps 10, 11, and 12 using the wax paper, polyethylene, and glass as covers for the small can. Record your data in the Data Table. **Caution: Do not try to put the lid around the pane of glass.**

Data and Observations

Data Table

Time (sec)	Temperature (°C)			
	Plastic wrap	Wax paper	Polyethylene	Glass

LAB 12 Graphing the Efficiency of Solar Collectors

Student Worksheet *(continued)*

14. Use colored pencils to make a scatter plot of the data for each cover material. Use a different color for each material. Display a key of the colors on your graph.

15. Draw the line of best fit through each scatter plot. The color of the line should match the color of the points.

Analysis

16. Which cover material is most efficient in collecting heat?

_____

How does your data support your conclusion?

_____

17. Describe the lines of best fit for each material. How do your lines compare with the STAT PLOT figures shown on the screen of your calculator? Print out the STAT PLOT for each material and include the labeled figures with your other data.

Graph 1

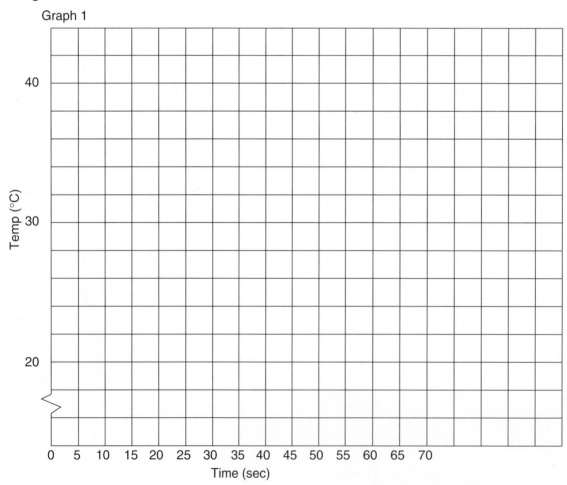

Graph 1

Wind Power and Box-and-Whisker Plots

Teaching Suggestions

Objectives

- Construct a device to measure wind speed.
- Measure the wind speed at different times during the day for a week.
- Display measurements in a box-and-whisker plot.
- Determine if wind is a good source of energy in your area.

Recommended Time

- 2 class periods; students collect data three times a day over a one-week time period.

Materials

- stiff cardboard (10 sheets)
- glue or paste
- sheet of grid paper (10)
- magic marker, any color (10)
- needle, long enough to go through ball (10)
- nylon line (10 pieces, 30 cm each)
- table tennis ball (10)
- scissors (10 pairs)

Preparation

- Gather materials.
- Check the area around the school building to find the best place for students to take their measurements of wind speed.

Teaching the Lab

- Have students work in groups of three or four, with students sharing the data collection task.
- Students should work together to construct the wind speed device. All group members should take the first set of measurements together so they each use the same technique in subsequent measurements. Verify that students are holding their devices level when they collect their first set of data.
- Students should use care when coloring the nylon line so that they don't inadvertently color the protractor.

Wind Power and Box-and-Whisker Plots

Teaching Suggestions *(continued)*

Data and Observations

Sample Data Table

Date/Time	Wind Speed (°)	Wind Speed (km/hr)	Date/Time	Wind Speed (°)	Wind Speed (km/hr)
	10	13		10	13
	20	19.2		10	13
	15	16		10	13
	15	16		15	16
	20	19.2		15	16
	20	19.2		15	16
	10	13		10	13

Analysis

Sample responses

8. 13 13 13 13 13 13 16 16 16 16 19.2 19.2 19.2

9. 16

10. upper quartile, $x = 17.6$

   lower quartile, $x = 13$

11. GV = 19.2

   LV = 13

12.

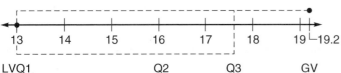

13. Answers will vary. For the sample data provided, wind power would be a practical source of electricity because the speed of wind is constantly above 12.8 km/hr.

Further Explorations

Have students find out more about how wind energy is converted to electric energy. Ask them to research whether or not wind is a practical source of energy for your area.

LAB 13

Wind Power and Box-and-Whisker Plots

Student Worksheet

Introduction

Some of the sun's energy combines with the rotation of the Earth to produce wind. Sometimes, people can use wind power to turn turbines and produce electrical energy. In order to use the wind as a source of energy, there must be a steady source of wind, usually of a constant speed of at least 12.8 kilometers per hour.

Objectives

- Construct a device to measure wind speed.
- Measure the wind speed at different times during the day for a week.
- Display measurements in a box-and-whisker plot.
- Determine if wind is a good source of energy in your area.

Materials

- stiff cardboard
- glue or paste
- sheet of grid paper (1)
- magic marker, any color (1)
- needle, long enough to go through ball (1)
- nylon line (30 cm)
- table tennis ball (1)
- scissors

Procedure

1. Cut out the protractor in Figure 1 and glue it to the cardboard.

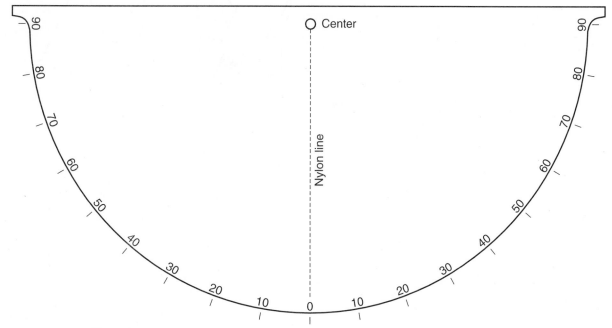

Figure 1

Wind Power and Box-and-Whisker Plots

Student Worksheet *(continued)*

2. Thread the nylon line through the needle and pull the thread through the center of the table tennis ball.

3. Tie a knot in the end of the nylon line and glue it to the ball. Glue the free end of the nylon line to the spot marked center on the protractor.

4. Color the nylon line with the magic marker.

5. Test the device by setting it alongside the edge of a flat surface. If it is level, the line should cover the 0° mark.

6. Select the windiest area around the school to measure the wind speed. Hold the device level and face the wind. Allow the wind to move the table tennis ball. See Figure 2. The angle made by the nylon line will be the wind speed in degrees. Measure the angle to the nearest 5° and record it in the Data Table.

7. Use the Conversion Table to convert your angle measure to km/hr. Write the converted measure in the Data Table.

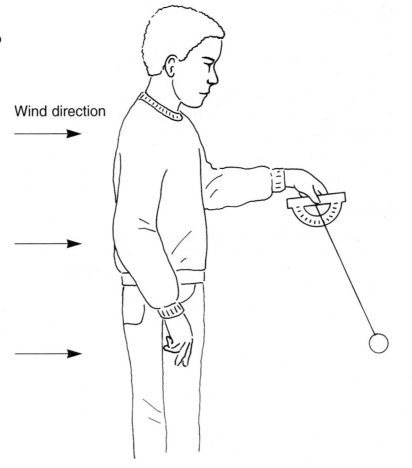

Wind direction

Figure 2

Wind Power and Box-and-Whisker Plots

Student Worksheet (continued)

Data and Observations

Data Table

Date/Time	Wind Speed (°)	Wind Speed (km/hr)	Date/Time	Wind Speed (°)	Wind Speed (km/hr)

Conversion Table

Angle	km/hr
0	0.0
5	9.6
10	13.0
15	16.0
20	19.2
25	20.8
30	24.0
35	25.6
40	28.8
45	32.0
50	33.6
55	36.8
60	41.6
65	46.4
70	52.8

Wind Power and Box-and-Whisker Plots

LAB 13

Student Worksheet *(continued)*

Analysis

8. Arrange your data in numerical order.

9. Find the median for your data.

10. Find the quartiles for your data.

11. Find the upper and lower extreme values for your data.

12. Draw a box-and-whisker plot for your data.

13. Use your data to analyze whether or not your area would be a good area for using wind to produce electricity.

Determining Percent Acetic Acid in Vinegar

Teaching Suggestions

Objectives

- Verify the concentration of acetic acid in vinegar using titration.
- Use a Texas Instruments graphics calculator and CBL™ unit to measure pH.
- Write and solve a system of linear equations based on data collected.

Recommended Time

- 1 class period

Materials

- distilled water
- NaOH pellets
- aprons (30)
- 1.0 M NaOH solution (1 liter)
- goggles (30 pairs)
- 250-mL beakers (10)
- gloves (30 pairs)
- 50-mL graduated cylinders (10)
- three different solutions of vinegar
- 50-mL burets and buret clamps (10)
- ring stands and utility clamps (10)
- CBL™ (10)
- magnetic stirrers and stirring bars or glass stirring rods (10)
- CBL-compatible calculators with unit-to-unit cables (10)
- Vernier pH probes with CBL™ DIN adapters (10) (Note: the Vernier CBL pH probe is not included with the CBL™ unit. Information about purchasing Vernier CBL pH probes is provided on page 4 of the CBL™ System Experiment Workbook.)

Preparation

- Prepare the 1.0 M NaOH solution by dissolving 40.0 grams of NaOH pellets in distilled water to produce 1 L of solution. **Caution: Do not handle NaOH pellets with your hands. Have students wear goggles, gloves, and an apron while doing this laboratory. NaOH spills should be treated by rinsing the affected area with tap water for 10 to 15 minutes.**
- You may need to calibrate the pH probes before students use them. To calibrate the probes, follow the instructions on page 5 of the CBL™ System Guidebook.

Determining Percent Acetic Acid in Vinegar

Teaching Suggestions *(continued)*

Teaching the Lab

- Students work in groups of three.

Data and Observations

Sample Data Table. Data is approximate, based on vinegar solutions of 3%, 4%, and 5%.

Brand or type of vinegar	A	B	C
Amount of vinegar used	35 mL	35 mL	35 mL
mL of NaOH used to reach a pH of 9	21.9 mL	30 mL	36.5 mL
Molarity (mol/l) of acetic acid in vinegar	0.6257 M	0.857 M	1.0427 M
Percentage of acetic acid in vinegar	3%	4%	5%

Analysis

15. 2.81 liters of the 3% solution and .19 liters of the 10% solution

16. Students should have graphed the line $y = x$. It takes one mole of NaOH to neutralize one mole of CH_3OOH.

Further Explorations

Vitamin C is the common name for ascorbic acid. Design an experiment to determine the amount of ascorbic acid in a Vitamin C tablet.

LAB 14

Determining Percent Acetic Acid in Vinegar

Student Worksheet

Introduction

In a titration, a known amount of a substance of known concentration is added to a known amount of a substance of unknown concentration. In most cases, a base is added to a sample of an acid, or the known solution is an acid, which is added to a base of unknown concentration. Small quantities of the known solution are added until the other solution has been neutralized completely.

In this experiment, you will determine the concentration of a solution of vinegar by titration. Vinegar is a dilute solution of acetic acid (CH_3CHOOH). The base used in this titration is sodium hydroxide, NaOH. The titration of this particular acid and base can be written:

$$CH_3COOH + NaOH \rightarrow NaCH_3COO + H_2O$$

Objectives

- Verify the concentration of acetic acid in vinegar using titration.
- Use a Texas Instruments graphics calculator and CBL™ unit to measure pH.
- Write and solve a system of linear equations based on data collected.

Materials

- apron
- goggles
- gloves
- three different brands of vinegar
- ring stand and utility clamp
- magnetic stirrer and stirring bar or glass stirring rod
- CBL™ compatible calculator with unit-to-unit cable
- Vernier pH probe with CBL™ DIN adapter (not included in the CBL unit)

- 1.0 M NaOH solution
- 250-mL beaker
- 50-mL graduated cylinder
- 50-mL buret and buret clamp
- Texas Instruments CBLTM unit

Procedure

Caution: Strong bases such as NaOH can cause severe burns. Wear goggles, gloves, and an apron while doing this laboratory! If NaOH spills on your skin or gets into your eyes, notify your teacher immediately and rinse the affected area with tap water for 10 to 15 minutes.

A. Set Up

1. Set up your CBL™ system. Use the unit-to-unit link cable to connect the CBL™ unit to your calculator. Use the I/O ports located on the bottom edge of each unit.
2. Attach the buret clamp to the ring stand. Place a buret in the clamp.
3. Use a utility clamp to attach the pH probe to the ring stand below the buret. Connect the other end of the pH probe to channel 1 (CH1) on the top edge of the CBL™ unit. Turn on the CBL™ unit and the calculator.
4. Download or enter the PH program from the disk accompanying your CBL™ Experiment Workbook or from the TI Web site.
5. Rinse the buret and tip with a small quantity of NaOH. Then, fill the buret to the 0.0 mL mark with 1.0 M of the NaOH solution.
6. Measure 35 mL of vinegar using a 50-mL graduated cylinder. Pour the vinegar into a 250-mL beaker. Record the brand of vinegar used in the Data Table of the Data and Observations section.
7. If you are using a magnetic stirrer, place the beaker on the stirrer. Then, place the beaker under the buret. Make sure that the pH probe is deep in the solution and does not touch the stirring bar.

B. Data Collection

8. Start the PH program on the calculator. The program will prompt you for the number of the channel the probe is connected to (1) and for the number of readings to take (enter 30).
9. At the ML? prompt, enter zero. Zero is the number of mL of NaOH that you have added to the vinegar so far. Press TRIGGER on the CBL™ to take a pH reading.

LAB 14 Determining Percent Acetic Acid in Vinegar

Student Worksheet (continued)

10. Each time the program prompts you with the ML? prompt, add 3–5 mL NaOH to the vinegar. Record on a sheet of paper the amount added. Enter the amount into the calculator. (Stir the vinegar briefly with the glass stirrer at this point if you are not using a magnetic stirrer.) Wait a few seconds to allow the reading to stabilize, and then press TRIGGER to take a pH reading.

11. After 18–20 mL of NaOH have been added, or the solution has reached a pH of about 5, decrease the amount of NaOH that you add to the vinegar to 1–2 mL per reading. Be sure to record the amount added for each reading. When the display shows that the pH = 9, the NaOH has neutralized the acetic acid in the vinegar. In Table 1, record the amount of NaOH you have added up to this point.

12. Discard the solution in the beaker and wash the beaker. Rinse the pH probe and set the equipment back in place. Repeat steps 5–12 for the two additional brands of vinegar.

Data and Observations
Data Table

Brand or type of vinegar			
Amount of vinegar used	35 mL	35 mL	35 mL
mL of NaOH used to reach a pH of 9			
Molarity (mol/l) of acetic acid in vinegar			
Percentage of acetic acid in vinegar			

13. Determine the molar concentration of CH_3OOH in each solution of vinegar using the equation: $M_1V_1 = M_2V_2$. Record your answers in the Data Table.

   $M_1 = 1.00$ M NaOH

   $V_1 = $ volume (in mL) of NaOH used in the titration to reach a pH of 9

   $M_2 = $ molar concentration of CH_3OOH

   $V_2 = $ volume (in mL) of vinegar used in each titration

14. Use the molar concentration of CH_3OOH in the solution to determine the amount of moles of CH_3OOH in the 35 mL sample of vinegar. Then, convert the moles of acetic acid to grams using

   the formula moles $CH_3OOH \times \dfrac{48}{1 \text{ mol } CH_3OOH} = $ grams CH_3OOH.

(Forty-eight is the gram formula mass of CH_3OOH.) Convert grams of CH_3OOH to mL by using vinegar's density: 1.001 gram/mL. Then divide your result by 35 mL to calculate the percentage of CH_3OOH in the vinegar. Record your answers in the Data Table.

Analysis

15. Sometimes chemists test levels of acidity in solutions because they need a solution with a particular level of acidity to use in an experiment. Suppose that you tested two vinegar solutions and found them to have acidity levels of 3% and 10%. But you need three liters of 6% acetic acid solution. Write a system of equations and solve it to find out how many liters of each solution you should mix to make the 6% solution.

_____

16. How many moles of NaOH does it take to neutralize one mole of CH_3OOH? Using the data for two of the solutions of vinegar, find the number of moles per liter of NaOH (x) and the number of moles per liter of CH_3OOH (y) used at the point of neutralization. Graph a line based on these data points. The slope of the line should equal the number of moles of NaOH it takes to neutralize one mole of CH_3OOH.

Scientific Notation and Astronomical Distances

Teaching Suggestions

Objectives

• Use scientific notation to express the distances in the solar system.
• Choose a scale to represent the distances in the solar system.
• Make a model to visually illustrate the distances between the sun and each of the planets.

Recommended Time

• 1 class period

Materials

• adding machine tape (15 rolls)
• meterstick (15)
• felt tip pen (15)
• scissors

Preparation

• Gather materials.

Teaching the Lab

• Have students work with partners.
• Suggest that students look at the maximum distance first when they are trying to choose a scale.

Data and Observations
Data Table

Planet	Average distance from sun (km)	Average distance from sun (km) expressed in scientific notation	Scale distance from sun (cm)
Mercury	58 000 000	5.8×10^7	5.8
Venus	108 000 000	1.08×10^8	10.8
Earth	150 000 000	1.50×10^8	15.0
Mars	229 000 000	2.29×10^8	22.9
Jupiter	777 000 000	7.77×10^8	77.7
Saturn	1 426 000 000	1.426×10^9	142.6
Uranus	2 876 000 000	2.876×10^9	287.6
Neptune	4 490 000 000	4.49×10^9	449.0
Pluto	5 914 000 000	5.914×10^9	591.4
Scale of distances 1 cm = 10 000 000 km			

Scientific Notation and Astronomical Distances

Teaching Suggestions (continued)

Analysis

5. Answers will vary, but students should mention that expressing large distances in scientific notation makes relative distances more obvious. Students can estimate a reasonable scale by looking first at the exponents.

6. The model can help students understand relative distances; the magnitude of the distances is not shown on the model.

7. Answers will vary, but should describe a scale that results in a model that shows distances between the planets and the sun without being impractically long.

8. About 2.6×10^7 years

Further Explorations

Have students use their models to draft maps of the solar system on grid paper. Their maps should have a scale, which may be different from the scale they used for their models.

LAB 15

Scientific Notation and Astronomical Distances

Student Worksheet

Introduction

Astronomers work with very large numbers in calculating distances in the universe. Light from our sun takes 8 minutes to reach Earth. Light emitted by the next closest star, Alpha Centauri, takes 4.3 years. How far is Alpha Centauri? The distance light travels in one year is about 9×10^{12} miles. The distance to Alpha Centauri is about 3.87×10^{13} miles. Can you imagine how far this distance is? Making a model is a good way to start.

Objectives

- Use scientific notation to express the distances in the solar system.
- Choose a scale to represent the distances in the solar system.
- Make a model to visually illustrate the distances between the sun and each of the planets.

Materials

- adding machine tape
- meter stick (1)
- felt tip pen (1)
- scissors

Procedure

1. Convert into scientific notation the distances between each planet and the sun. Add your answers to the Data Table.

2. Choose a scale to use in your model of the distances between the planets and the sun. (By expressing the distances in scientific notation, you will make it easier to decide on a scale.) Determine the scale distance for each planet. Record your answers in the Data Table.

3. Place a dot at one end of the adding machine tape to represent the sun. Figure out how long your piece of tape needs to be to fit the planets to scale. Cut the correct amount of adding machine tape from the roll.

4. Use the scale distance to find the position of each planet on the adding machine tape. Place a dot along the tape for each planet. Label each dot with the name of the planet it represents.

LAB 15 Scientific Notation and Astronomical Distances

Student Worksheet (continued)

Data and Observations
Data Table

Planet	Average distance from sun (km)	Average distance from sun (km) expressed in scientific notation	Scale distance from sun (cm)
Mercury	58 000 000		
Venus	108 000 000		
Earth	150 000 000		
Mars	229 000 000		
Jupiter	777 000 000		
Saturn	1 426 000 000		
Uranus	2 876 000 000		
Neptune	4 490 000 000		
Pluto	5 914 000 000		
Scale of distances			

Analysis

5. How did converting the distances into scientific notation help you make your model?

_____

6. What can your model show about distances in space? What doesn't your model show?

_____

_____

7. What scale did you choose? Why did you choose this scale?

_____

_____

8. A round trip to the moon requires about one week of Earth time. The moon is about 3.86×10^5 km away. At this rate, how long would it take to get to Alpha Centauri from Earth?

_____

_____

Projectile Motion

Teaching Suggestions

Objectives

- Use the Texas Instruments Calculator-Based Laboratory System (CBL™) to measure flight time and height of a projectile.
- Model a projectile's motion algebraically using a quadratic equation.
- Analyze the trajectory of a projectile in motion using quadratic equations.

Recommended Time

- 1 class period

Materials

- buckets of water (15)
- goggles (15 pairs)
- toy water rockets and launchers (15)
- CBL™ and compatible calculator with a unit-to-unit cable (15)
- Vernier CBL motion detectors (15) (Note: the Vernier CBL motion detector is not included with the CBL™ unit. Information about purchasing Vernier CBL motion detectors is provided on the TI Web site.

Preparation

- Toy water rockets are available at most toy shops and hobby shops.

Teaching the Lab

- Have students work in pairs.
- If possible, the rockets should be launched straight up, not at an angle, because the motion detector detects motion in a limited range and because students are collecting data on height and time.
- Students may need to repeat flights of the rocket if they have difficulty launching the rocket so that it will remain in range of the motion detector.
- You may wish to have students download their graphs into a computer and print them out.
- If students need help in assembling the CBL™ system, you can refer them to the CBL™ System Guidebook.

Data and Observations

11. Answers will vary.

highest height: several feet

time elapsed: 2–3 seconds

time elapsed from beginning to end of flight: 4–5 seconds

Analysis

12. Answers will vary. Students should recognize that the time up and the time down were almost equal to each other.

13. Answers will vary, but students should recognize that the velocity of the rocket is included in their equations in the same position that the variable b appears in the equation $y = ax^2 + bx + c$.

14. Answers will vary, but students should algebraically reach the same answers they recorded in their data collection. Students should show their work.

15. Answers will vary, but students should reach the same answer using both methods. Students should show their work.

Further Explorations

Will a projectile continue to fall faster and faster toward Earth? Does the size or shape of a projectile affect its motion? How does the air affect a projectile moving through it? Choose a question and answer it using reference materials and through experimentation. Write a brief report explaining the answer to the question.

LAB 16 Projectile Motion

Student Worksheet

Introduction

What do a baseball, a jumping ballerina, and a rocket have in common? Each goes up into the air and comes back down again. At least temporarily, anything that is thrown or launched into the air is a projectile.

The path followed by a projectile is called a trajectory. Figure 1 shows the shape of the trajectory of a toy rocket. The motion of the projectile is up and then down. Figure 2 shows the size and direction of the vertical velocity of a toy rocket at different moments along its trajectory. The rocket's upward velocity begins to decrease immediately after launch and the rocket begins to slow down. Then, for an instant at the highest point of its trajectory, it stops moving because its upward velocity is zero. The rocket immediately begins to fall and its downward velocity increases as it falls.

As you can see, the downward trajectory of the rocket mirrors the shape of the upward trajectory. The entire trajectory forms the shape of a parabola. (Baseballs flying through the air also follow a parabola-shaped path.) In this experiment, you will collect data about the motion of projectiles and use your data to model a projectile's motion algebraically.

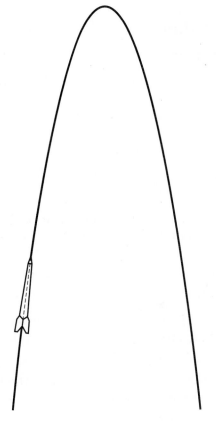

Figure 1

Objectives

- Use the Texas Instruments Calculator-Based Laboratory System (CBL™) to measure flight time and height of a projectile.
- Model a projectile's motion algebraically using a quadratic equation.
- Analyze the trajectory of a projectile in motion using quadratic equations.

Materials

- bucket of water
- toy water rocket and launcher
- CBL-compatible calculator with a unit-to-unit cable
- Vernier CBL motion detector
- goggles
- CBL™ unit

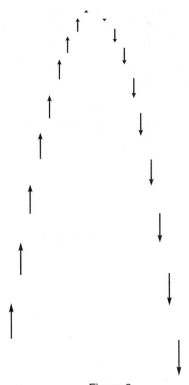

Figure 2

Lab 16

LAB 16 Projectile Motion

Student Worksheet *(continued)*

Procedure

A. Set Up

1. Read through the procedure and decide who will be responsible for each step. One person must operate the rocket, and one person must operate the CBL and calculator. Both partners must wear goggles during this experiment.

2. Set up your CBL™ system. Use the unit-to-unit link cable to connect the CBL™ unit to your calculator. Use the I/O ports located on the bottom edge of each unit.

3. Connect the motion detector to the SONIC port on the left side of the CBL, and place the motion detector on the ground in an open area, facing up.

4. Download or enter the HIKER program from the disk accompanying your CBL™ Experiment Workbook or from the TI Web site.

5. Fill the water rocket to the level line shown on the rocket's body. Make sure to fill the rocket to the same level during each flight in the experiment.

6. Attach the pump/launcher to the rocket as shown in the manufacturer's directions.

B. Rocket Launch

7. Pump the pump/launcher 10 times. **Caution: do not exceed 20 pumps or the maximum number suggested by the manufacturer, whichever is lower. Be sure to hold the rocket and pump/launcher so that the rocket is not directed toward yourself or another person.** While the rocket operator is pumping, the CBL operator should turn on the CBL and start the program HIKER on the CBL-compatible calculator.

8. At the prompt, the CBL operator should press ENTER to start the graph. The motion detector will start clicking. The rocket operator should then launch the rocket over the motion detector, being careful to keep the rocket in the motion detector's beam.

9. Observe the flight of the rocket. If the falling rocket seems likely to hit the motion detector, move the motion detector out of the way—but don't move the motion detector until the rocket has clearly begun to fall. Retrieve the rocket and repeat steps 5–9 if necessary.

LAB 16 Projectile Motion

Student Worksheet *(continued)*

Data and Observations

10. The HIKER program will save the time and height (distance) data to lists L2 and L3 on the calculator. When the program is finished, it will generate a graph of the data.

11. Your graph will contain a downward-facing parabola. Trace the parabola by pressing TRACE and moving the cursor with the arrow keys. Find the highest height the rocket reached and the time it took to reach that height. Then find the time elapsed from the beginning of the flight to the end. Remember that x = time elapsed in seconds, while y = height in feet.

highest height: _____

time elapsed: _____

time elapsed from beginning to end of flight: _____

Analysis

12. Did your graph support the statement that the time for a projectile to reach its highest point is equal to the time for the projectile to fall back to Earth? Explain.

_____

_____

_____

13. The flight of a projectile can be described by the equation $h = vt - 16t^2$, where h = height (distance), t = time, and v = initial upward velocity. What was the initial upward velocity of the rocket?

_____

14. Use the formula $h = vt - 16t^2$ to determine how long the rocket should have stayed in the air and what its height should have been at the middle of its flight. Show your work on the lines below. Then check your work against your data of how long the rocket actually stayed in the air and what its height actually was at the middle of its flight.

_____

_____

_____

Lab 16

LAB
16

Projectile Motion

Student Worksheet   (continued)

15. The height of the rocket can also be described by the function
$h(t) = vt - 16t^2$. Find the height of the rocket after 3 seconds.
Then, divide the polynomial in the function by $t - 3$ to illustrate
the remainder theorem. Show your work on the lines below. Then check
your work by tracing your graph on the calculator to find the
value y when $x = 3$.

_____

_____

_____

_____

_____

_____

LAB 17 Overproduction
Teaching Suggestions

Objectives
- Count the number of seeds in one green pepper.
- Use the class data to calculate the average number of seeds in one green pepper.
- Make a function table to predict the size of the green pepper population after four years of overproducing.
- Graph your function.

Recommended Time
- 1 class period

Materials
- green peppers (15)
- plastic knives, serrated edge (15)
- paper towels

Preparation
- Gather materials. Some green peppers are seedless. Be sure you have peppers with seeds.
- If you don't want students to use plastic knives, you could cut the peppers in half before you distribute them.

Teaching the Lab
- Have students work with partners. To save time, each partner can count a portion of the seeds in one pepper. Partners then add the number of seeds in the portions together to arrive at a total.

Overproduction

Data and Observations

Sample Table

Function Table

x (generation)	y (seeds)
1	(100) (1×10^2)
2	(10 000) (1×10^4)
3	(1 000 000) (1×10^6)
4	(100 000 000) (1×10^8)
5	(10 000 000 000) (1×10^{10})

Analysis

5. Data suggests that pepper plants overproduce.

6. If you start with just one pepper plant, after four generations, you will have 1×10^8 pepper plants!

7. In nature, many seeds do not develop into new plants. Seeds might be eaten by animals, or conditions, such as temperature, water availability, sunlight, and so forth, may not be right for germination and development.

8. For the fifth generation, the population would be 1×10^{10}.

Further Explorations

Have students graph their data. They will need to consider the scale for the *y*-axis carefully as the numbers increase rapidly.

LAB 17 Overproduction

Student Worksheet

Introduction

Most living things overproduce. Flowering plants are good examples of overproduction. If all of the seeds from all the flowering plants developed into new plants, we'd soon have far too many plants growing around us. That's what overproduction means.

Objectives

- Count the number of seeds in one green pepper.
- Use the class data to calculate the average number of seeds in one green pepper.
- Make a function table to predict the size of the green pepper population after four years of overproducing.
- Graph your function.

Materials

- green pepper (1)
- plastic knife (1)
- paper towels

Procedure

1. Cut open the green pepper and count the number of seeds inside. Record this number in the Data and Observations section.

2. Find out how many seeds your classmates found. Use the class data to find the average number of seeds in one pepper. Round the class average to the nearest 100.

3. To analyze the reproduction of green peppers, make the following assumptions:

   a. Only one green pepper plant existed in your area during the first year.

   b. Each seed produced by a green pepper plant grows into a new green pepper plant the next year.

   c. Each new green pepper plant produces the same number of seeds as the class average.

4. The reproduction of seeds over several years is an exponential function $y = 1 \times 10^{2x}$, where x equals the number of generations after the first plant. Use this formula to complete the Function Table.

Lab 17

LAB 17

Overproduction

Student Worksheet (continued)

Data and Observations

Number of seeds in my green pepper   _____

Total number of class green pepper seeds   _____

Total number of peppers in the class   _____

Class average (rounded to the nearest 100)   _____

Function Table

x (generation)	y (seeds)
1	
2	
3	
4	
5	

Analysis

5. What does your data suggest about reproduction in pepper plants?

_____

6. Use your data about green peppers and the function to explain overproduction.

_____

7. What conditions in nature keep plants from overproducing?

_____

8. What would the green pepper population be for the fifth generation?

_____

Physical Factors of Soil

Teaching Suggestions

Objectives
- Determine the amounts of various particle types in three soil samples.
- Use formulas to calculate the water contents and water-holding capacities of three soil samples.

Recommended Time
- 2 class periods

Materials
- soil samples (30)
- 20-cm cloth squares (30)
- scoops (10)
- water
- balances (several)
- specimen jars with lids (30)
- pins (30)
- beakers (30)
- metric rulers (10)
- masking tape (10 rolls)

Preparation
- Have each student bring a soil sample in a plastic bag. Explain to the students that soil water will not be lost if samples are sealed in plastic bags.

Teaching the Lab
- Have students work in groups of three, with each student collecting data on one sample.
- If 100-mL graduated cylinders are available, add 50 mL of loose soil to the cylinder. Add 50 mL of water and shake as directed. The amount of various mineral particles can be determined by direct reading.
- Soil samples can be dried in a warm oven for several hours or in an incubator overnight.
- In Parts B and C, students actually measure the water-holding capacity and water content of the soil and the cloth, but the water content and water-holding capacity of the cloth is small and so it can be ignored.
- To keep the pan of the balance dry when massing a wet soil sample, have students place the sample in a cup made from aluminum foil. The mass of the aluminum foil will be negligible compared with the soil and can be ignored.

Physical Factors of Soil

Teaching Suggestions *(continued)*

Data and Observations

Sample Tables:

Table 1

Soil Particle Size Data					
	Amount of each particle type (in mm)				
Soil location	Gravel	Coarse sand	Fine sand	Silt	Clay
1. Oak forest	20	10	8	40	12
2. Garden soil	46	11	21	16	12
3. Cow pasture	20	12	9	35	10

Table 2

Water Content and Water-holding Capacity					
Soil location	Mass of soil and cloth	Mass of dried soil and cloth	Mass of saturated soil and cloth	Percentage water content	Percentage water-holding capacity
1. Oak forest	125 g	95 g	250 g	31.6%	163%
2. Garden soil	150 g	105 g	175 g	42.9%	66.7%
3. Cow pasture	135 g	120 g	145 g	12.5%	20.8%

Analysis

10. **a.–b.** Answers will vary with soil sample used.

11. **a.** clay and silt

    b. sand and gravel

12. Loosely packed soil allows water to drain through it. Closely packed soil does not drain as well.

Further Explorations

- Research the procedure for calculating the organic-matter content of a soil sample.

- Prepare a chart showing the predominant soil types in various parts of the United States. Show how soil types affect the commercial activities of an area.

LAB 18

Physical Factors of Soil

Student Worksheet

Introduction

Soil is a major factor influencing the survival of many living things. Many organisms live in the soil. Others are anchored in soil and obtain water and minerals from it. Still other organisms depend on these soil-dependent organisms for food. The physical properties of a particular kind of soil determine the kinds of plants that grow in the soil and the kinds of animals that live in or on it.

Objectives

• Determine the amounts of various particle types in three soil samples.
• Use formulas to calculate the water contents and water-holding capacities of three soil samples.

Materials

• soil samples (3)
• beakers (3)
• balance
• specimen jars with lids (3)
• 20-cm cloth squares (3)
• masking tape
• water
• metric ruler
• pins (3)
• scoop

Procedure

A. Particle Size

1. Label three specimen jars with the locations of the soil samples. Fill each jar halfway with soil. Add water, allowing it to soak into the soils, until the jars are full.

2. Cover the jars with lids and shake until the large soil particles break apart. Set the jars aside and let the particles settle overnight.

3. Using a ruler, measure the depth of each particle type in each jar.

4. Record in Table 1 the amounts of gravel, coarse sand, fine sand, silt, and clay in the settled soil samples. See the drawing at the right.

B. Water Content

5. Soak the cloth squares in water. Attach labels identifying the samples with pins.

6. Place a scoop of soil in each cloth. Wrap the soil samples in the wet cloths. Determine and record their masses in Table 2. Place the wrapped samples where they will dry completely, then redetermine and record their masses. Calculate the water content of each sample as a percentage of the dry mass of soil.

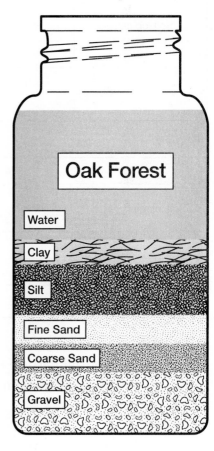

$$\text{percentage water content} = \frac{\substack{\text{mass of} \\ \text{soil and cloth}} - \substack{\text{mass of dried} \\ \text{soil and cloth}}}{\substack{\text{mass of dried} \\ \text{soil and cloth}}} \times 100$$

Lab 18

LAB 18

Physical Factors of Soil

Student Worksheet (continued)

C. Water-Holding Capacity

7. Place each dried soil sample and cloth from Part B in a beaker of water for five to ten minutes or until the soil is saturated.

$$\text{percentage water-holding capacity} = \frac{\text{mass of saturated soil and cloth} - \text{mass of dried soil and cloth}}{\text{mass of dried soil and cloth}} \times 100$$

8. Remove the wrapped samples from the beakers and allow excess water to drain from them through the cloths. Find and record the masses of the saturated samples.

9. Calculate the water-holding capacity of each sample as a percentage of the dry mass.

Data and Observations

Table 1

Soil Particle Size Data					
	Amount of each particle type (in mm)				
Soil location	Gravel	Coarse sand	Fine sand	Silt	Clay
1.					
2.					
3.					

Table 2

Water Content and Water-holding Capacity					
Soil location	Mass of soil and cloth	Mass of dried soil and cloth	Mass of saturated soil and cloth	Percentage water content	Percentage water-holding capacity
1.					
2.					
3.					

Analysis

10. Which type of soil particle made up:

    a. the greatest amount of each soil sample? _____

    b. the least amount? _____

11. Which type of soil particle was:

    a. most closely packed? _____

    b. least closely packed? _____

12. How does the type of soil particles affect water drainage? _____

_____

Tracking Hurricanes

LAB 19

Teaching Suggestions

Objectives

- Plot the paths of two hurricanes.
- Compare the paths of two hurricanes.
- Use the distance formula to find the distance between the starting and ending points of the hurricanes.

Recommended Time

- 1 class period

Materials

- red and blue pencils (15–30 of each)

Teaching the Lab

- This activity could be assigned as an independent assignment, homework, or as a cooperative project done with two students in each group.

Data and Observations

Sample map:

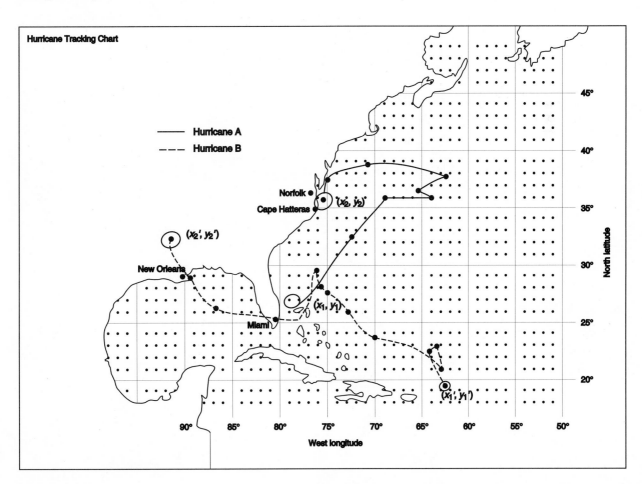

Analysis

4. Coordinates may vary slightly. 38°N, 75°W; 36°N, 75°W

5. Coordinates may vary slightly. 25.5°N, 77°W; 26°N, 80°W; 29.5°N, 90°W

6. North

7. Hurricane A: $d = 9.05°$, about 1,005 km

Hurricane B: $d = 31.5°$, about 3,497 km

8. Hurricanes do not generally move in a straight path. Using the distance formula only gives you the distance between two points. Because the hurricanes turn and change direction, the actual distance traveled is greater than the distance between the beginning and end points.

Further Explorations

Have students do research to find the coordinates of a more recent hurricane. They can add the path of the more recent hurricane to their maps.

LAB 19 Tracking Hurricanes

Student Worksheet

Introduction

Hurricanes are violent storms that form over water in the zone of the Trade Winds. Hurricanes produce strong winds, high seas, and heavy rain. If they reach land, they do great damage.

It's important to follow the path of a hurricane. The U.S. Weather Bureau begins to report a *hurricane watch* when a hurricane reaches a position where it seems likely to endanger land areas. The watch begins a few days before the hurricane is expected to reach land. A *hurricane warning* is different—in a hurricane warning, all precautions should be taken immediately to protect life and property. In this activity, you will use a coordinate grid to keep track of two hurricanes. Then you will use the distance formula to find the distance between the starting points and ending points of the hurricanes.

Objectives

- Plot the paths of two hurricanes.
- Compare the paths of two hurricanes.
- Use the distance formula to find the distance between the starting and ending points of the hurricanes.

Materials

- pencils (red, blue)

Procedure

1. On the hurricane tracking chart in the Data and Observations section, use the red pencil to plot the path of Hurricane A for each day. Use the data in Table 1.

2. On the same tracking chart, plot the path of Hurricane B for each day. Plot the path with the blue pencil. Use the data in Table 2.

3. Circle the beginning and the end point on the path of each hurricane.

LAB 19 Tracking Hurricanes

Student Worksheet (continued)

Data and Observations

Table 1. Hurricane A

Date (September, 1967)	Position (at 7:00 A.M.)	
	Latitude	Longitude
9	27.5°N	79°W
10	30.5°N	77.5°W
11	36°N	71°W
12	36°N	66°W
13	36.5°N	64.5°W
14	37.5°N	65.5°W
15	38.5°N	68°W
16	38°N	74.5°W
17	36°N	76°W

Table 2. Hurricane B

Date (August–September, 1965)	Position (at 7:00 A.M.)	
	Latitude	Longitude
29	19.5°N	63.5°W
30	22.5°N	65.5°W
31	23°N	66.5°W
1	21°N	67°W
2	23.5°N	70°W
3	26°N	73°W
4	28°N	75°W
5	28.5°N	76°W
6	29.5°N	76°W
7	25.5°N	78°W
8	25.5°N	81°W
9	26.5°N	87°W
10	29.5°N	90.5°W
11	33°N	92°W

LAB 19

Tracking Hurricanes

Student Worksheet *(continued)*

Analysis

4. At which coordinates did Hurricane A hit land? (Note: There may be more than one pair of coordinates.)

_____

5. At which coordinates did Hurricane B hit land? (Note: There may be more than one pair of coordinates.)

_____

6. In which general direction, north or south, do hurricanes move?

_____

7. Use the distance formula to calculate the distance between the starting and ending points of each hurricane. Multiply your answer in degrees by 111 km per degree to determine the distance in kilometers.

8. Is the distance formula helpful for analyzing how far a hurricane travels? Why or why not?

_____

_____

_____

LAB 19 Tracking Hurricanes

Student Worksheet (continued)

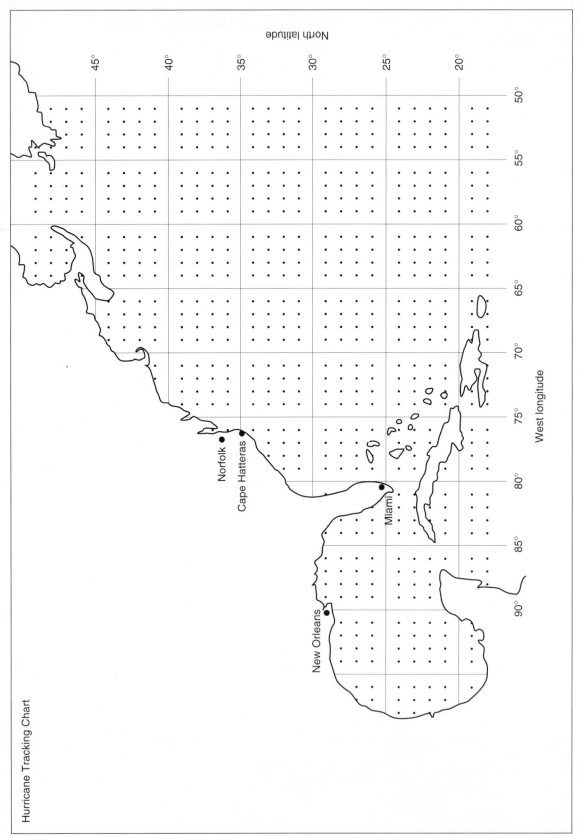

Hurricane Tracking Chart

North latitude

West longitude

A Mathematical Look at Cell Size

Teaching Suggestions

Objectives

- Build cell models.
- Use formulas to determine the surface area, volume, and mass of each cell model.
- Use ratios to determine the relationship between the surface area and volume of each cell model.
- Use ratios to determine the relationship between the surface area and mass of each cell model.

Recommended Time

- 1 class period

Materials

- photocopies of 3 cell models (included in student pages (15))
- white glue (15 bottles)
- scissors (30)
- balance (several)
- coarse sand (1 bag)
- small scoops (several)

Preparation

- If possible, photocopy the cell models on heavy paper. The heavier the paper, the sturdier the models will be and the less likely they will be to break when filled with sand.

Teaching the Lab

- Have students work in pairs. Each member of the pair should participate in assembling the models, calculating measurements and ratios, and recording data.
- Refer students to the figure on page 64 so that they know how to assemble the models. Remind students that they should imagine that there is a sixth side to the models.
- Encourage students to carefully fold and glue their cell model, as this will affect the accuracy of their mass measurement.

A Mathematical Look at Cell Size

Teaching Suggestions *(continued)*

Data and Observations

Table 1

		Measurements of Cell Models		
Cell size (length of one side, s)	Area for one face: $A = s^2$	Total surface area of cell: (area of one face) × (the total number of faces)	Volume of cell: $A = s^3$	Mass of cell (grams)
1	1	6	1	Answers
2	4	24	8	will
4	16	96	64	vary.

Table 2

	Ratios of Cell Model Measurements	
Cell size (length of one side)	Total surface area to volume	Total surface area to mass
1	6:1	Answers will vary.
2	3:1	Surface-area-to-mass ratio
4	1.5:1	will decrease as size increases.

Analysis

7. The paper represents the cell membrane. The sand represents the cytoplasm.

8. As a cell grows larger and accumulates more contents, it will need more surface area to accommodate the growth. It will need more cell membrane to get materials into and out of the cell.

9. As cells grow larger, surface-area-to-volume ratio gets smaller.

10. While answers for the surface-area-to-mass ratio will vary among students depending on their mass measurements, students should find the ratio also gets smaller.

11. the smallest cell

12. 27

13. 27 cells, each with $s = 1$.

Further Explorations

Investigate actual cell sizes by using a microscope. Use a micrometer to measure the cell diameter, or estimate cell size from the size of the microscope's field of view.

LAB 20

A Mathematical Look at Cell Size

Student Worksheet

Introduction

Like all cells, the cells in your body are continuously dividing to make new cells. This process allows your body to continue growth, form reproductive cells, and repair tissues. Cells generally grow until they reach a certain size and then divide. Why don't cells continue to grow indefinitely? To answer this question, apply formulas about surface area, volume, and mass to cell models of various sizes.

Objectives

- Build cell models.
- Use formulas to determine the surface area, volume, and mass of each cell model.
- Use ratios to determine the relationship between the surface area and volume of each cell model.
- Use ratios to determine the relationship between the surface area and mass of each cell model.

Materials

- photocopy of 3 cell models
- white glue
- scissors
- balance
- coarse sand
- small scoop

Lab 20

A Mathematical Look at Cell Size

LAB 20

Student Worksheet (continued)

Procedure

1. Work with a partner to build models of cells. Cut out the three cell models. Fold and glue together all sides of each model. You will have three structures that resemble open boxes, as shown below. Imagine that each cell model has a sixth side and is a closed box. These models represent a cell at three different stages of growth. The model that is 1 unit to a side represents the earliest stage of growth. The model that is 4 units to a side represents the latest stage in growth.

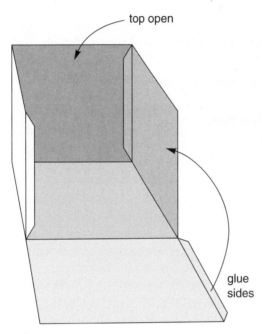

top open

glue
sides

2. Use the formulas in Table 1 to calculate the area for one face, the total surface area, and the volume for each cell model. In each formula, *s* represents the length in number of units of one side of your model. Record your calculations in Table 1.

3. Carefully fill each cell with sand.

4. Determine the mass of each sand-filled cell model by using the balance. Record the masses in the last column of Table 1.

5. Calculate the ratio of total surface area to volume for each cell model. To do this, divide the cell's total surface area by its volume. Record your answers in Table 2.

6. Calculate the ratio of total surface area to mass for each model cell. To do this, divide the cell's total surface area by its mass. Record your answers in Table 2.

A Mathematical Look at Cell Size

LAB 20

Student Worksheet *(continued)*

Lab 20

Data and Observations

Table 1

Measurements of Cell Models				
Cell size (length of one side, *s*)	Area for one face: $A = s^2$	Total surface area of cell: (area of one face) × (the total number of faces)	Volume of cell: $A = s^3$	Mass of cell (grams)
1				
2				
4				

Table 2

Ratios of Cell Model Measurements		
Cell size (length of one side)	Total surface area to volume	Total surface area to mass
1		
2		
4		

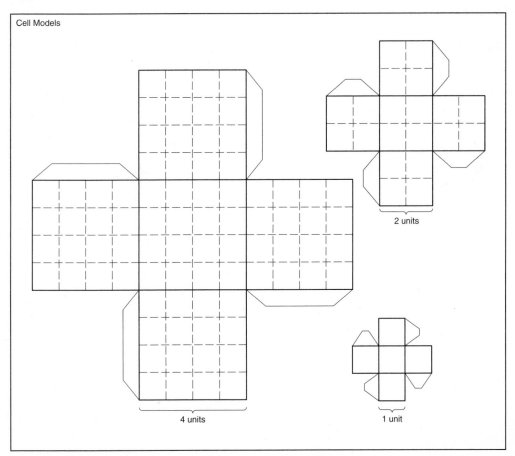

Cell Models

2 units

4 units

1 unit

LAB 20 A Mathematical Look at Cell Size

Student Worksheet (continued)

Analysis

7. What parts of your cell model represent parts of an actual cell?

_____

_____

8. As a cell grows larger and accumulates more contents, will it need more or less cell membrane to survive? Explain your answer.

_____

_____

9. As a cell grows larger, does the surface-area-to-volume ratio get larger, get smaller, or remain the same?

_____

_____

10. As a cell grows larger, what happens to the surface-area-to-mass ratio?

_____

_____

11. Which cell model has the greatest surface-area-to-volume and surface-area-to-mass ratios?

_____

_____

12. How many cells with $s = 1$ fit into a cell with $s = 3$?

_____

_____

13. Which has more total surface area, one cell with $s = 3$ or 27 cells, each with $s = 1$?

_____

_____

The Effect of a Solute on Freezing Point

Teaching Suggestions

Objectives
- Use the Texas Instruments Calculator-Based Laboratory System (CBL™) to measure temperature.
- Determine the effect of solute concentration on the freezing point of a solute.
- Show the relationship between amount of solute in a solution and freezing point by graphing data points in a scatter plot and drawing a line of best fit, or regression line, using a CBL™ compatible calculator.
- Write a prediction equation based on data points.

Recommended Time
- 1 class period

Materials
- aprons (30)
- goggles (30)
- notebook paper (75 sheets cut in half)
- shaved or crushed ice
- NaCl
- TI temperature probes (15)
- CBL™ compatible calculator with unit-to-unit cable (15)
- rubber bands (15)
- ketchup cups (30) with lids (15)
- paper punches (15)
- balances (15)
- CBL™ units (15)
- TI-GRAPH LINK (optional) (15)

Preparation
Use shaved or crushed ice, not ice cubes.

Teaching the Lab
- Have students work in pairs.
- Make sure that students have read and understood the purpose, procedure, and safety precautions for this laboratory before they proceed.
- Remind students not to overload the calorimeter with ice. The top must fit securely on the calorimeter.
- Remind students that they must work quickly with the ice/calorimeter combination. If they work too slowly so that no ice remains in the calorimeter, the addition of more NaCl will not give the expected decrease in temperature.

97 *Science and Mathematics Lab Manual*

The Effect of a Solute on Freezing Point

Teaching Suggestions *(continued)*

Data and Observations

Answers may vary slightly.

Mass of calorimeter (with lid)   2.34 g

Mass of calorimeter and ice   17.44 g

Sample Data Table

	Reading 1	Reading 2	Reading 3	Reading 4	Reading 5	Reading 6
NaCl mass (g)	0	0.25	0.50	0.75	1.00	1.25
Temperature (°C)	−1	−2.2	−3.0	−4.2	−5.0	−6.1
Moles of NaCl	0	0.0043	0.0085	0.013	0.017	0.021
Moles of ions	0	0.0086	0.017	0.026	0.034	0.042
Moles of ions/ kilogram of ice	0	0.57	1.1	1.7	2.3	2.8

20. Using the sample data in the table results in an equation of $y = -1.7726007413252x - 1.081011953496$ for the regression line. With this equation, students would find a temperature of −8.2°C for 4 moles of ions per kilogram of ice.

Analysis

21. As NaCl was added, the temperature of the mixture decreased.

22. As more NaCl was added, more ice melted.

23. As more NaCl was added, the freezing point of the solution decreased.

Further Explorations

- Research the effect of a solute on boiling point, and design an experiment that measures that effect.

- Research the importance of boiling point and freezing point in cooking and preparing food. Use your research and what you have learned about the effect of a solute on boiling and freezing points to explain something about the preparation of food. For example, you might want to explain why ice cream does not freeze into a solid block. Or, you could explain why cooks often add salt to water before they boil it.

LAB 21

The Effect of a Solute on Freezing Point

Student Worksheet

Introduction

Pure water freezes at 0°C at standard atmospheric pressure. At this point, the vapor pressures of liquid water and solid water are the same. If there is a nonvolatile compound—a compound that will not evaporate unless it is boiled—dissolved in the water, however, the solution will not freeze until the temperature is lower than 0°C. Only at a lower temperature will the vapor pressure of the solid equal the lowered vapor pressure of the liquid. Freezing point lowering, like boiling point elevation, is dependent only on the concentration of solute particles, not on the kind of solute that is used.

Objectives

- Use the Texas Instruments Calculator-Based Laboratory System (CBL™) to measure temperature.

- Determine the effect of solute concentration on the freezing point of a solute.

- Show the relationship between amount of solute in a solution and freezing point by graphing data points in a scatter plot and drawing a line of best fit, or regression line, using a CBL™ compatible calculator.

- Write a prediction equation based on data points.

Materials

- apron
- goggles
- 5 half sheets of notebook paper
- shaved or crushed ice
- NaCl
- TI temperature probe
- CBL-compatible calculator with a unit-to-unit cable
- rubber band
- ketchup cups (2) with lid (1)
- paper punch
- balance
- CBL unit
- TI-GRAPH LINK (optional)

Procedure

A. Calorimeter

1. Prepare five samples of NaCl. Use the balance to measure each sample. Make sure that each sample has a mass of 0.25 g, and place the samples on separate pieces of paper.

2. Construct a plastic calorimeter—a device for measuring heat changes. Put a rubber band around the middle of one ketchup cup and then place this cup inside a second ketchup cup. See Figure 1 at right. Use a paper punch to make a hole in the lid of a ketchup cup.

hole made by hole puncher

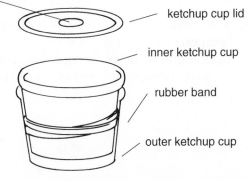
ketchup cup lid

inner ketchup cup

rubber band

outer ketchup cup

LAB 21 The Effect of a Solute on Freezing Point

Student Worksheet (continued)

3. Use the balance to measure the mass of the empty calorimeter and its lid. Record the mass in the Data and Observations section.

4. Set up your CBL™ system. Use the unit-to-unit link cable to connect the CBL™ unit to your calculator. Use the I/O port located on the bottom edge of the unit.

5. Connect the temperature probe to Channel 1 (CH1) on the top edge of the CBL unit. Download or enter the HEAT program from the disk accompanying your CBL™ Experiment Workbook or from the TI Web site.

B. Temperature Changes

6. From this point on, you must work quickly. Read through steps 8–13 before beginning the next step so that you will be prepared for action. Decide with your partner how you will work together to complete each step smoothly.

7. Fill the calorimeter with crushed ice and replace the lid. Remove some ice if the top does not fit snugly.

8. Measure the mass of the calorimeter with its lid and ice. Record this mass in the Data and Observations section.

9. Insert the temperature probe through the hole in the calorimeter top. Start the program HEAT on the calculator. Enter 10 when the program prompts you for the amount of time to wait between each reading. After you enter the time between points, wait to press ENTER again until the program prompts you to do so. After you press ENTER, the CBL will collect data every ten seconds for six minutes. Observe the variations in temperature on the calculator display as data is collected. Record the first temperature in the Data Table under Reading 1.

10. After the CBL has taken six temperature readings, open the calorimeter and add one of the prepared NaCl samples. Replace the cover and the temperature probe. Swirl the calorimeter to mix the contents until the NaCl is completely dissolved. Remove the cover very briefly to check.

11. After every sixth temperature reading, repeat step 10 with another NaCl sample. Because the CBL will take six readings per minute, you must add NaCl once every minute. Observe the ice as more NaCl is added.

12. The calculator will save the temperature data in list L4. View the list of temperature data by pressing STAT 1. Use the arrow keys to move to list L4 and to move up and down. Record the lowest temperature reading for each change in NaCl mass in the Data Table.

LAB 21 The Effect of a Solute on Freezing Point

Student Worksheet *(continued)*

13. For each reading, convert grams of NaCl to the number of moles of NaCl and record the results in the Data Table. Use the formula

$$\text{grams NaCl} \times \frac{1 \text{ mol NaCl}}{\text{gfm NaCl}} = \text{mol NaCl}$$

Gfm refers to gram formula mass. The gram formula mass for NaCl is 68.5.

14. For each reading, calculate the number of moles of ions (moles NaCl × 2 ions/mole). Record the results.

15. Calculate the mass, in grams, of ice you started with and convert to kilograms.

_____

16. Complete the Data Table for moles of ions per kilogram of ice in each reading.

17. Enter the six readings for temperature and moles of ions/kilogram of ice into the STAT list editor. (Be sure to clear the existing lists first.) Use column L1 for moles of ions/kilogram of ice and column L2 for temperature.

18. Draw a scatter plot using the data you entered in step 17. First, change the window parameters. Use a viewing window of [0, 3] by [−6.5, −0.5] with Xscl = .5 and Yscl = .5. Then press [2nd] [STAT PLOT]. Press 1 to select Plot 1. After checking to be sure that the Xlist is L1 and the Ylist is L2, press [ENTER] and [GRAPH] .

19. Draw a line of best fit. Press [STAT] and then select the CALC menu. Select LinReg (ax + b) and then press [ENTER] . The variable a displayed on the calculator is the slope of the line of best fit. Press [Y=] and [VARS] . Select Statistics (5) and then use the right arrow key to highlight EQ. Select RegEQ and press [ENTER] and [GRAPH] .

20. Use the TRACE feature to predict the temperature of the mixture for 4 moles of ions/kilogram of ice. (You will need to adjust the viewing window first.)

_____

Lab 21

The Effect of a Solute on Freezing Point

LAB 21

Student Worksheet (continued)

Data and Observations

Mass of calorimeter (with lid): _____ g

Mass of calorimeter and ice: _____ g

Data Table

	Reading 1	Reading 2	Reading 3	Reading 4	Reading 5	Reading 6
NaCl mass (g)	0	0.25	0.50	0.75	1.00	1.25
Temperature (°C)						
Moles of NaCl						
Moles of ions						
Moles of ions/ kilogram of ice						

Analysis

21. What happened to the temperature of the mixture as NaCl was added?

_____

_____

22. What happened to the amount of ice remaining as NaCl was added?

_____

_____

23. What conclusion can you draw from the answers you gave to questions 21 and 22?

_____

_____

Caloric Content and Box-and-Whisker Plots

Teaching Suggestions

Objectives
- Calculate the number of Calories and grams of carbohydrates, fats, and proteins for two meals.
- Compare the nutritional value for each meal by plotting data on box-and-whisker plots.

Recommended Time
- 1 class period

Teaching the Lab
- Have students work in pairs. Each student should participate in calculating the Calories for each food item and plotting the data.
- If you don't have enough food tables, students can share copies.
- You may want to review the difference between a food Calorie and a scientific calorie. A food Calorie is actually a kilocalorie and is thus spelled with a capital C.
- Students can use calculators to speed up calculations.
- If necessary, you may want to review how to use the food table and calculate the Caloric values.

Data and Observations
Table 2

Calories and Nutrients of Two Sample Meals					
Food	Serving size	Calories	Carbohydrates (grams)	Fats (grams)	Proteins (grams)
Meal 1					
Spaghetti w/meat sauce	1 serving	396	39.4	20.7	12.7
Green beans	1 cup	31	6.8	.2	2.0
Garlic bread	2 slices	116	21.8	1.2	3.6
Butter	1 Tbsp	100	trace	11.4	trace
Gelatin	1 cup	163.5	39.6	trace	3.3
Total		806.5	107.6	33.5	21.6
Meal 2					
Hamburger bun	1	89	15.9	1.7	2.5
Ground beef	$\frac{1}{4}$ lb	224	0	14.5	21.8
Cheese (American)	1 oz	107	.5	8.4	6.5
Catsup	2 Tbsp	36	8.6	.2	.6
French fries	24	528	80.88	20.16	8.64
Cola-type beverage	10 oz	97.5	25.5	0	0
Total		1081.5	131.38	44.96	40.04

Caloric Content and
Box-and-Whisker Plots

Teaching Suggestions *(continued)*

Table 3

Meal 1	Calories	Carbohydrates	Fats	Proteins
Q_1	65.5	3.4	0.1	1.0
Q_2	116	21.8	1.2	3.3
Q_3	279.75	39.5	16.05	8.15
Range	365	39.6	20.7	12.7
Interquartile Range	214.25	36.1	15.95	7.15

Meal 1—Box-and-Whisker Plot

 proteins

 fats

carbohydrates

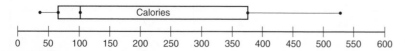

Calories

0 25 50 75 100 125 150 175 200 225 250 275 300 325 350 375 400

Meal 2	Calories	Carbohydrates	Fats	Proteins
Q_1	62.5	0.25	0.1	0.3
Q_2	102.25	12.25	5.05	4.5
Q_3	376	53.19	17.33	15.22
Range	492	80.88	20.16	21.8
Interquartile Range	313.5	52.94	17.23	14.92

Meal 2—Box-and-Whisker Plot

 proteins

carbohydrates

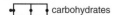 fats

Calories

0 50 100 150 200 250 300 350 400 450 500 550 600

Analysis

4. Calories: Meal 2; fats: Meal 2; carbohydrates: Meal 2; proteins: Meal 2.

Further Explorations

Prepare a meal plan for a day that meets the recommended daily intake
values of Calories, carbohydrates, fat, and protein. Calculate the Calories
and nutrient amounts for each item. Then graph the data on a box-and-
whisker plot. Compare the data with that from the two meals in the first
part of this lab.

LAB 22 Caloric Content and Box-and-Whisker Plots

Student Worksheet

Introduction

How do the foods you eat compare in nutrients such as carbohydrates, protein, and fat? By using a food table, you can calculate the nutrition in your daily meals.

Nutrients supply your body with raw materials for the manufacturing of new tissues and energy for daily functions. The energy stored in food is measured in Calories. One way to compare the amounts of nutrients in your meals is by using box-and-whisker plots.

Objectives

• Calculate the number of Calories and grams of carbohydrates, fats, and proteins for two meals.

• Compare the nutritional value for each meal by plotting data on box-and-whisker plots.

Procedure

1. Table 2 presents two separate lunch plans. Use Table 1 to determine the number of Calories in each food item listed. If Table 1 and Table 2 list different serving sizes, you will have to calculate the correct number of Calories for the serving in your meal plan.

2. Record your information, including the totals, in Table 2.

3. Compare the caloric and nutritional values of each meal using a box-and-whisker plot. Calculate Q_1, Q_2, Q_3, the range, and the interquartile range for each of the graphs. Record the data in Table 3. Make two plots, one for each meal, for each of the following: Calories, carbohydrates, fats, and proteins. If you have nutrient amounts listed as "Trace," substitute zero for the amount when making plots. Draw your plots on a separate sheet of paper.

Lab 22

LAB 22 Caloric Content and Box-and-Whisker Plots

Student Worksheet *(continued)*

Table 1

Food Values of Common Serving Sizes					
Food	Serving size	Calories	Carbohydrates (grams)	Fats (grams)	Proteins (grams)
Cola beverage	1 glass 8 oz	78	20.4	--	--
Toasted French bread	1 slice	58	10.9	.6	1.8
Spaghetti with meat sauce	1 serving	396	39.4	20.7	12.7
Hamburger roll	1	89	15.9	1.7	2.5
Butter, dairy	$\frac{1}{2}$ Tbsp	50	trace	5.7	trace
Cheese, American	1 oz	107	.5	8.4	6.5
Cooked green beans	1 cup	31	6.8	.2	2.0
Gelatin, Lemon	$\frac{2}{3}$ cup	109	26.4	trace	2.2
Ground beef	$\frac{1}{4}$ lb	224	0	14.5	21.8
French fries	10	220	33.7	8.4	3.6
Tomato catsup	1 Tbsp	18	4.3	.1	.3

LAB 22 Caloric Content and Box-and-Whisker Plots

Student Worksheet *(continued)*

Data and Observations

Table 2

Calories and Nutrients of Two Sample Meals					
Food	Serving size	Calories	Carbohydrates (grams)	Fats (grams)	Proteins (grams)
Meal 1					
Spaghetti w/meat sauce	6 oz				
Green beans	4 oz				
Garlic bread	2 slices				
Butter	1 Tbsp				
Gelatin	4 oz				
Total					
Meal 2					
Hamburger bun	1				
Ground beef	4 oz				
Cheese (American)	1 oz				
Catsup	2 Tbsp				
French fries	24				
Cola-type beverage	10 oz				
Total					

Lab 22

LAB 22 Caloric Content and Box-and-Whisker Plots

Student Worksheet (continued)

Table 3

Meal 1	Calories	Carbohydrates	Fats	Proteins
Q_1				
Q_2				
Q_3				
Range				
Interquartile Range				

Meal 2	Calories	Carbohydrates	Fats	Proteins
Q_1				
Q_2				
Q_3				
Range				
Interquartile Range				

Analysis

4. Which of the two meal samples in Table 2 is higher in:

   Calories? _____ fats? _____ carbohydrates? _____ proteins? _____

5. How does the data characterize the meals?

6. Look at each graph. Is the data concentrated over a narrow range of values or is the data more diverse?

7. Mark any outliers on the graph by circling the points. What do they represent?

Determining the Avogadro Constant

Teaching Suggestions

Objectives
- Collect a sample of butane and determine its molar volume at standard conditions.
- Calculate an approximate value for the Avogadro constant.
- Work with scientific notation to perform calculations with large numbers.

Recommended Time
- 1–2 class periods

Materials
- aprons (30)
- large beakers or pneumatic troughs (15)
- goggles (30)
- butane lighters (15)
- barometers (15)
- balances (15)
- thermometers (15)
- paper towels
- 100-mL graduated cylinders (15)

Preparation
- Students will need large containers to hold water for their inverted graduated cylinders. Pneumatic troughs, if available, work well for holding water. Warn students about the dangers of handling beakers of such large size.
- Any commercial butane cigarette lighter can be used, and lighters can be used again in the classes that follow. The lighters may be saved and reused from year to year.

Teaching the Lab
- **Safety precaution: No open flames should be permitted in the laboratory while this experiment is going on.**
- Have students work in pairs. Before proceeding, be sure students understand the purpose, procedure, and safety precautions for this laboratory activity.
- Remind students that with the tools available to them, the procedure can yield only an approximate value for the Avogadro constant.
- The most common problem in this laboratory procedure is finding a mass for the collected butane that is too low. This problem occurs when students do not dry the butane lighter thoroughly. A droplet of water trapped in the valve assembly of the lighter has enough mass to distort the results. Be sure to caution students to dry their lighters completely before finding the final mass.

Determining the Avogadro Constant

Teaching Suggestions *(continued)*

- Students may have the idea that the molar volume of the gas is always equal to 22.4 L. Point out to them that the molar volume depends on the temperature and pressure, and that STP (standard temperature and pressure) are used as universally understood conditions for comparing volumes.

- A large portion of the lab time will be devoted to calculations and analysis. Be sure to provide that time.

- Disposal: if necessary, students should vent the used butane gas in a fume hood.

Data and Observations

Sample data:

Barometric pressure	745 mm Hg (milimeters of mercury)
Initial mass of lighter	17.81 g
Temperature of water	23°C
Volume of gas	0.100 L
Final mass of lighter	17.55 g

11. 99.3 kPa

12. 0.26 g

13. 0.0045 mol

14. 96.5 kPa

15. 296 K

16. 0.0879 L

17. 19.5 L/mol

Analysis

18. 1.7×10^{-19} cm^3

19. 1.1×10^{23} molecules/mol

20. Students' answers will vary, depending on their results.

Further Explorations

A supercomputer can count at the rate of one billion (1×10^9) per second. To the nearest million, calculate how many years it would take for this computer to count up to the Avogadro constant.

LAB 23 Determining the Avogadro Constant

Student Worksheet

Introduction

One mole of any substance contains 6.02×10^{23} atoms, molecules, or formula units. This extremely large number of particles is known as the Avogadro constant. To calculate the Avogadro constant, you divide the molar volume, or the volume occupied by one mole of a gas, by the volume occupied by one molecule.

The volume occupied by one molecule of butane includes the space occupied by the atoms that make up butane, but also the space required for the molecule to move around. (Molecules take up more space when they are in motion, just as a person doing a cartwheel takes up more space than the same person standing still.) Because gas molecules move in straight lines and only change direction when they collide with other particles, the space occupied by a butane molecule is in the shape of a cylinder. (See the figure to the right.) The diameter of the cylinder equals the estimated diameter of a butane molecule, 4.5×10^{-8} cm. The height of the cylinder equals the mean free path of the molecule, assigned an average value of 1×10^{-4} cm. The mean free path is the average distance traveled by the molecule before a collision.

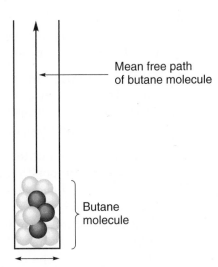

Mean free path of butane molecule

Butane molecule

Diameter of butane molecule

In this laboratory activity, you will measure the molar volume of butane (C_4H_{10}) and calculate the Avogadro constant. The experiment is not precise and the value it gives is only an approximation. Your value, therefore, may differ from the exact value. Because the numbers you are working with are so large, you will use scientific notation.

Objectives

- Collect a sample of butane and determine its molar volume at standard conditions.
- Calculate an approximate value for the Avogadro constant.
- Work with scientific notation to perform calculations with large numbers.

Materials

- apron
- goggles
- barometer
- thermometer
- 100-mL graduated cylinder
- large beaker or pneumatic trough
- butane lighter
- balance
- paper towel

Lab 23

LAB 23 Determining the Avogadro Constant

Student Worksheet (continued)

Procedure

1. Find the atmospheric pressure by reading a barometer or obtain the value from your teacher. Record the value in the Data and Observations section.

2. Determine the mass of a butane lighter to the nearest 0.01g. Record the mass in the Data and Observations section.

3. Add water to the large beaker or pneumatic trough until it is half full. Measure the temperature of the water in the beaker or trough and record it in the Data and Observations section.

4. Fill the 100-mL graduated cylinder all the way to the top with tap water. Invert the water-filled graduated cylinder in the beaker so that the top is under water. Hold it in place as shown in Figure 1. There should be no air trapped in the cylinder.

5. Hold the butane lighter under the water with the valve in the position shown in Figure 1 so that you can release gas from the lighter into the cylinder. As the gas rises into the cylinder, the water in the cylinder will be pushed out to make way for the gas. Press the valve and release gas until the cylinder is filled with a little less than 100 mL of the gas. Remove the lighter from the water and place it on a paper towel to dry.

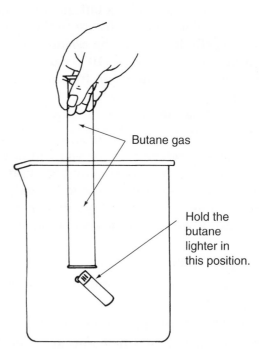

Butane gas

Hold the butane lighter in this position.

6. Adjust the cylinder in the beaker until the water levels inside and outside the cylinder are equal. This assures that the pressure of the gas inside the cylinder is the same as atmospheric pressure. Hold the cylinder in that position and read the volume of the trapped gas to the nearest milliliter. Record the volume in liters in the Data and Observations section.

7. Release the gas from the graduated cylinder as your teacher instructs.

8. Dry the lighter very thoroughly. Use a paper towel or tissue to get rid of any water trapped in the valve area of the lighter. Do this very carefully; even a little trapped water will affect results.

9. Determine the mass of the dried lighter and record it in the Data and Observations section.

10. Rinse the graduated cylinder, and pour the water in the beaker down the drain.

LAB
23

Determining the Avogadro Constant

Student Worksheet *(continued)*

Data and Observations

Barometric pressure _____ mm Hg (milimeters of mercury)

Initial mass of lighter _____ g

Temperature of water _____ °C

Volume of gas _____ L

Final mass of lighter _____ g

11. Convert the atmospheric pressure to kilopascals. (Pascals are a standard unit used to measure pressure.)

$$\text{Pressure (kPa)} = \frac{\text{atmospheric pressure}}{7.50 \text{ mm Hg}}$$

$P_{total} =$ _____

12. Calculate the mass of butane collected.

Mass = initial mass of the lighter − final mass of the lighter

= _____

13. Calculate the number of moles of butane collected. The molar mass of butane is 58.

$$n = \frac{\text{mass of butane collected}}{\text{molar mass of butane}}$$

= _____

14. Determine the pressure of dry butane collected. ($P_{water} = 2.8$ kPa)

$$P_{dry\ gas} = P_{total} - P_{water}$$

= _____

15. Convert the water temperature to a Kelvin temperature. Recall that absolute zero on the Kelvin scale is about −273°C on the Celsius scale.

Temperature (K) = temperature of water + 273

= _____

Lab 23

LAB 23 Determining the Avogadro Constant

Student Worksheet *(continued)*

16. The combined gas law states that $\dfrac{P_1 \times V_1}{T_1} = \dfrac{P_2 \times V_2}{T_2}$ where

P = pressure, V = volume, and T = temperature. Use the following form of the combined gas law to calculate the volume that the collected butane would occupy at STP (standard temperature and pressure).

$$V = \frac{\text{volume of gas} \times P_{\text{dry gas}} \times 273 \text{ K}}{101.3 \text{ kPa} \times \text{water temperature in Kelvins}}$$

= _____

17. Calculate the molar volume of the butane gas collected in this experiment.

$$\text{Molar Volume} = \frac{\text{volume of gas collected at STP}}{\text{number of moles of gas collected}}$$

= _____

Analysis

18. Find the volume of a hypothetical cylinder occupied by one butane molecule. Assume that the molecule has a diameter of 4.5×10^{-8} cm and travels the mean free path distance of 1.0×10^{-4} cm/molecule.

Volume of cylinder
= $\pi \times (\text{radius})^2 \times$ height of cylinder swept by one molecule
= $\pi \left(\dfrac{\text{molecular diameter}}{2} \right)^2 \times$ mean free path

= _____

19. Find the Avogadro constant.

$$\text{Avogadro constant} = \frac{\text{molar volume (L/mol)} \times 1000 \text{ cm}^3/\text{L}}{\text{volume of cylinder (cm}^3/\text{molecule)}}$$

= _____

20. How does your result compare with the correct value of 6.02×10^{23}?

_____

_____

_____

LAB 24 How Does Temperature Affect Mealworm Metamorphosis?

Teaching Suggestions

Objectives
- Observe the four stages of the life cycle of the mealworm, *Tenebrio*.
- Use the Texas Instruments Calculator-Based Laboratory System (CBL™) to measure temperature.
- Conduct an experiment to test the effect of temperature on the development of a mealworm from the pupa to the adult stage.
- Determine the standard deviation for the number of days it takes an adult mealworm to emerge at room temperature and at 30°C.

Recommended Time
- 1 class period, then five minutes a day until all adult mealworms have emerged (about two weeks)

Materials
- samples of mealworms (egg, larva, pupa, adult) (8 of each)
- mealworm pupae (of same age) (32)
- wax marking pencils (8)
- stereomicroscopes (8)
- plastic vials (32)
- foam plugs (32)
- incubator (at 30°C)
- CBL™ and compatible calculator with a unit-to-unit cable
- TI temperature probe

Preparation
- Start a large mealworm culture in a five-gallon bucket. Fill the bucket $\frac{1}{2}$ to $\frac{2}{3}$ full of bran meal. Place 25 to 30 mealworms, acquired from a pet shop or biological supply house, in the bucket on top of the bran meal. Crinkle paper towels to cover the bran. Place 4 to 5 apple or potato slices on top of the paper towels. Change the slices every week or so.
- To ensure that each student's pupae are the same age, culture the larvae until they pupate and collect the pupae daily. New pupae are white; they turn yellowish-brown as they mature.
- If you prefer, purchase mealworm larvae or pupae from a biological supply house.

Teaching the Lab
- Have students work in groups of four.
- After adult mealworms emerge and are recorded, students can add them to the culture pail.
- Students may be confused by the different names used for mealworms. *Tenebrio* is the genus name. Mealworm and darkling beetle are common names for the same insect.
- If students need help in assembling the CBL™ system, you can refer them to the CBL™ System Guidebook.

How Does Temperature Affect Mealworm Metamorphosis?

Teaching Suggestions *(continued)*

Data and Observations

Answers may vary.

Sample Table 1

Tenebrio Metamorphosis		
Temperature	Starting date	Length of time for emergence (days)
Room temp. A		12
Room temp. B		14
30°C A		6
30°C B		8

Sample Table 2

Calculations			
Temperature	Total number of days for entire class	Total number of pupae for entire class	Mean time for emergence
Room temp. (21°C)	206	16	13
30°C	115	16	7

Analysis

9. Based on the above data, the standard deviation for the number of days it takes an adult mealworm to emerge either at room temperature or at 30°C is 1 day.

10. An increase in temperature decreased the length of time for metamorphosis.

11. Many observations are more accurate than only a few. The pupae may not all be exactly the same age, so an average age is used. The experiment called for each group to have two vials for each temperature so that more data would be gathered—if only one vial was used, there would be only eight samples for the entire class.

Further Explorations

- Repeat the investigation with other insects, such as Drosophila, to see if temperature affects their metamorphosis.

- Design an experiment to test the effect of temperature on other stages in the life cycle of *Tenebrio*.

LAB 24

How Does Temperature Affect Mealworm Metamorphosis?

Student Worksheet

Introduction

Many living things exist in different forms throughout their life cycles. Metamorphosis is the process of changing from one form to another. Some insects, such as moths, mealworms, and beetles, undergo complete metamorphosis, existing as egg, larva, pupa, and adult forms. The mealworm, *Tenebrio,* is an excellent insect for the study of complete metamorphosis.

Objectives

- Observe the four stages of the life cycle of the mealworm, *Tenebrio.*
- Use the Texas Instruments Calculator-Based Laboratory System (CBL™) to measure temperature.
- Conduct an experiment to test the effect of temperature on the development of a mealworm from the pupa to the adult stage.
- Determine the standard deviation for the number of days it takes an adult mealworm to emerge at room temperature and at 30°C.

Materials

- samples of mealworms (egg, larva, pupa, adult)
- mealworm pupae (of same age) (4)
- wax marking pencil
- stereomicroscope
- plastic vials (4)
- foam plugs (4)
- incubator (at 30°C)
- CBL™ compatible calculator with a unit-to-unit cable
- TI temperature probe

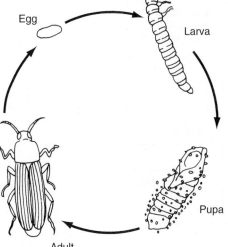

Egg
Larva
Pupa
Adult

Procedure

1. Examine samples of the four stages of mealworms under the stereomicroscope. Identify each sample using the chart of the life cycle of *Tenebrio.*

2. With your marking pencil, label the four plastic vials Room Temp. A, Room Temp. B, 30°C A, and 30°C B. These labels indicate the temperature at which the pupae will be stored. Label them also with your name (or group name) and the date.

3. Place one pupa in each of the four vials and stopper with foam rubber plugs. The foam plugs will allow the insects to breathe.

4. Store your vials at their proper temperatures with those of the rest of the class. Record the starting date in Table 1.

5. Set up your CBL™ system. Use the unit-to-unit link cable to connect the CBL™ unit to your calculator. Use the I/O port located on the bottom edge of the unit.

 Science and Mathematics Lab Manual

LAB 24 How Does Temperature Affect Mealworm Metamorphosis?

Student Worksheet *(continued)*

6. Connect the temperature probe to Channel 1 (CH1) on the top edge of the CBL unit, and turn on the CBL unit and the calculator. Download or enter the HEAT program from the disk accompanying the CBL™ Experiment Workbook or from the TI Web site. Take the room temperature and record it in Table 2.

7. Check your vials daily for the presence of adult mealworms. When you observe an adult in a vial, record in Table 1 the number of days needed for metamorphosis. Follow your teacher's directions for disposing of mealworms.

8. When metamorphosis of all the mealworms is complete, compile the class data and complete Table 2. Calculate the average time for emergence by dividing the total number of days by the total number of pupae.

Data and Observations

Table 1

Tenebrio Metamorphosis		
Temperature	Starting date	Length of time for emergence (days)
Room temp. A		
Room temp. B		
30°C A		
30°C B		

Table 2

Calculations			
Temperature	Total number of days for entire class	Total number of pupae for entire class	Mean time for emergence
Room temp. (_____°C)			
30°C			

Analysis

9. Determine the standard deviation for the number of days it takes an adult mealworm to emerge at room temperature and at 30°C.

_____

10. How did an increase in temperature affect the time needed for metamorphosis?

_____

11. Why might the class mean be a more accurate measurement of the time for metamorphosis than your data alone? Why did the experiment call for you to use two vials for each temperature?

_____

Symmetry in Parabolas and Animals

Teaching Suggestions

Objectives

- Identify the symmetry of a variety of organisms.
- Relate symmetry in organisms to lines of symmetry in parabolas.

Recommended Time

- 1 class period

Materials

- photocopy of Figure 1 for each student (30)
- grid paper (30 sheets)

Teaching the Lab

- Have students work individually in this lab.

Data and Observations

Answers for the Data Table will vary, depending on how students display each organism on a grid.

Sample Data Table

Organism	Symmetry	Parabolic formula	Axis of symmetry	Vertex	Focus	Directrix
Horseshoe Crab	bilateral	$y = -\dfrac{4}{25}x^2 + 4$	$x = 0$	0, 4	$0, 2\dfrac{7}{16}$	$y = 5\dfrac{9}{16}$
Turtle	bilateral	$y = -\dfrac{4}{25}x^2 + 6$	$x = 0$	0, 6	$0, 4\dfrac{7}{16}$	$y = 7\dfrac{9}{16}$
Scorpion	bilateral	$y = -\dfrac{8}{25}x^2 + 7$	$x = 0$	0, 7	$0, 6\dfrac{7}{32}$	$y = 7\dfrac{25}{32}$
Dog	bilateral	$y = -\dfrac{5}{8}x^2 + 12\dfrac{1}{2}$	$x = 0$	$0, 12\dfrac{1}{2}$	$0, 12\dfrac{1}{10}$	$y = 12\dfrac{9}{10}$
Sea Star	bilateral	$y = -\dfrac{7}{50}x^2 + 4$	$x = 0$	0, 4	$0, 2\dfrac{3}{14}$	$y = 5\dfrac{11}{14}$
Skate	bilateral	$y = -\dfrac{5}{16}x^2 + 6$	$x = 0$	0, 6	$0, 5\dfrac{1}{5}$	$y = 6\dfrac{4}{5}$
Millipede	bilateral	$y = -1\dfrac{7}{9}x^2 + 6$	$x = 0$	0, 3	$0, 2\dfrac{55}{64}$	$y = 3\dfrac{9}{64}$

Further Explorations

- Make a list of other animals that exhibit symmetry.
- Research information about how the behavior of an organism is affected by symmetry.

Symmetry in Parabolas and Animals
Student Worksheet

Introduction

Think of an imaginary line beginning at the top of your head, running between your eyes, and continuing down the center of your body. The part of your body that is to the right of this line mirrors the part of your body to the left of it. Organisms that can be divided into mirror-image halves along a central plane are bilaterally symmetrical. Organisms with parts that radiate from a central point or from a central axis have radial symmetry.

You can find many examples of symmetry in nature. You've encountered symmetry in mathematics. Take another look at symmetry as you do this lab.

Objectives

- Identify the symmetry of a variety of organisms.
- Relate symmetry in organisms to lines of symmetry in parabolas.

Materials

- photocopy of Figure 1 (1)
- grid paper (1)

Procedure

1. Study the organisms drawn in Figure 1. Identify the type of symmetry that characterizes each organism's body plan and record it in the Data Table. Draw a line through the center of each organism to help you make the identifications.

2. Use the following information to categorize the organisms. Then record your observations in the Data Table.

   - Can the organism be divided along any plane into roughly equal halves? If so, classify the organism as radially symmetrical.

   - Can the organism be divided along only one line going through its center to form mirror-image halves? Then the organism is bilaterally symmetrical.

3. Display each of the organisms in Figure 1 as a parabola. Carefully cut out each drawing and place it on grid paper. Place the organism's line of symmetry along the y-axis with the widest horizontal part along the x-axis. Label the uppermost point on the y-axis the vertex, and draw a parabola that curves around the organism. Repeat this procedure for the rest of the organisms in Figure 1.

4. Determine a formula for the parabolas and record each formula in the Data Table. Identify the axis of symmetry, the vertex, the focus, and the directrix.

Symmetry in Parabolas and Animals

Student Worksheet (continued)

Figure 1

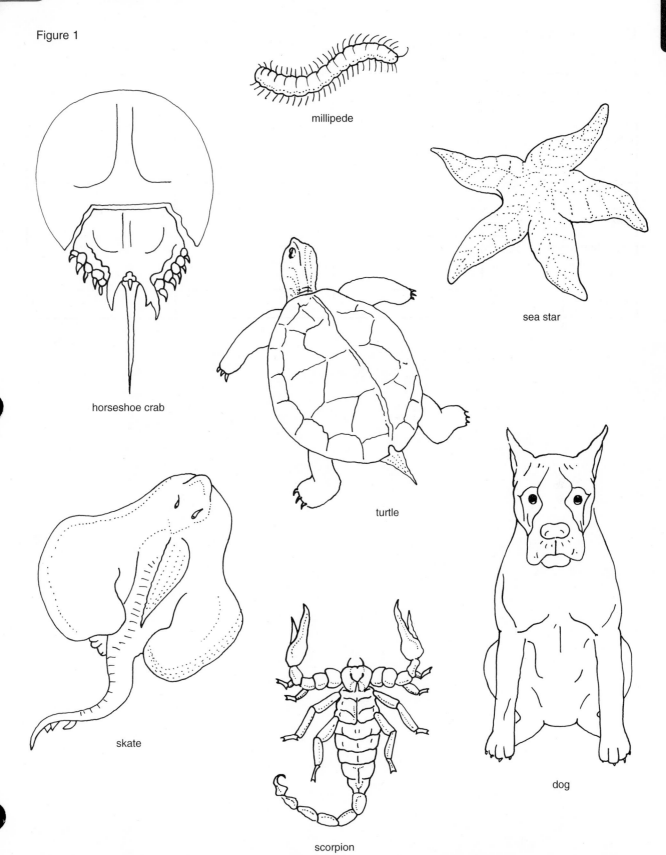

millipede

sea star

horseshoe crab

turtle

skate

scorpion

dog

Symmetry in Parabolas and Animals

**LAB
25**

Student Worksheet   *(continued)*

Data and Observations

Data Table

Organism	Symmetry	Parabolic formula	Axis of symmetry	Vertex	Focus	Directrix
Horseshoe Crab						
Turtle						
Scorpion						
Dog						
Sea Star						
Skate						
Millipede						

Rates of Diffusion of Gases

LAB 26

Teaching Suggestions

Objectives

- Measure the distances two gases move.
- Use inverse relations to calculate the masses and velocities of two gases.
- Compare the two ratios.

Recommended Time

- 1 class period

Materials

- concentrated HCl
- test tubes (30)
- goggles (30 pairs)
- clear plastic straws (30)
- one-hole rubber stoppers (30)
- metric rulers (15)
- scissors (15 pairs)

- concentrated NH_3
- solid stoppers (30)
- aprons (30)
- double-ended cotton swabs (15)
- 250-mL beakers (15)
- clear tape

Preparation

- Have students work in pairs.
- Do not allow students to handle the supply bottles of concentrated acid and base. Instead, for each pair, prepare 0.5-mL samples in small, stoppered test tubes.
- Keep samples in a fume hood to prevent escape of vapor into the room.
- Plastic straws must be clear. Students will not be able to observe the white ring through an opaque straw.
- Prepare proper waste receptacles for solutions and disposable equipment before the lab begins.

Teaching the Lab

- **Caution: Have students put on goggles and aprons before beginning the lab. Both HCl and NH_3 can cause skin burns; irritate eyes, nose, and lungs; and damage clothing.**
- You may want to point out to students that while all particles of matter are in motion, gas molecules exhibit the greatest amount of motion.
- Air currents can affect the results of this experiment. Make sure windows are closed and no fans are running.
- Have on hand a bottle of $NaHCO_3$ to neutralize an HCl spill. Have 2M acetic acid for NH_3 spills.

- **Disposal:** All solutions, water, and excess acid should be mixed together to neutralize. The waste solution should be collected in a polyethylene dishpan or similar container devoted to that purpose. Retain the solutions until the end of the period or day. In the fume hood, set up a hot plate with a 1-L or 2-L beaker. Pour the collected solutions into the beaker. Turn the hot plate on low and allow the beaker to heat with the hood running and the hood door closed. The liquids and volatiles in the mixture will evaporate, leaving dried chemicals. Allow the beaker to cool. Continue to add solutions and waste until the beaker is $\frac{2}{3}$ full. Treat the waste as heavy metal waste. *Dispose of the beaker and its dry contents in an approved manner.* Soak the swabs in water before disposing of them. The straws can be discarded without any treatment.
- Provide students with the molecular mass of HCl and NH_3 listed below.

Data and Observations

1. Distance NH_3 moved _18_ cm   **2.** Distance HCl moved _11_ cm

3. Molecular mass of NH3 _17_ g/mole   **4.** Molecular mass of HCl _36_ g/mole

Analysis
(Sample data are used.)

5. The ratio $\frac{d_1}{d_2}$ is $\frac{18}{11}$, or 1.64.

$$\left(\frac{\text{distance } NH_3 \text{ moved}}{\text{distance HCl moved}} = \frac{18 \text{ cm}}{11 \text{ cm}} = 1.64 \right)$$

6. Using the information from #1, $\sqrt{\dfrac{m_2(\text{HCl})}{m_1(NH_3)}} = 1.64$. Thus,

$\dfrac{m_2(\text{HCl})}{m_1(NH_3)} = 1.64^2 = 2.7.$

Using the known values, $\dfrac{m_2(\text{HCl})}{m_1(NH_3)} = \dfrac{36}{17} = 2.1.$

7. (Students should be able to hypothesize that the lighter gas, NH_3, will diffuse faster than the heavier gas, HCl.) The molecules of NH_3 had the greater velocity. The molecules of HCl have the greater mass. Lighter molecules move faster than more massive ones.

8. The distance a gas moves is inversely proportional to the square root of the mass of gas molecules; the greater the mass of the molecules, the smaller the distance the molecules move in a given time.

Further Explorations

Hydrogen gas is the most abundant element in the universe. Oxygen gas is a relatively rare element in the universe. On Earth, hydrogen is never found uncombined. Oxygen makes up about one-fifth of Earth's atmosphere. Use Graham's law to explain this difference between the two gases on Earth.

LAB 26 Rates of Diffusion of Gases

Student Worksheet

Introduction

Even if you are in another room, you can tell when someone has sliced a lemon or an onion in the kitchen because particles of the lemon or onion move through the air. This movement of particles of one substance through another medium (in this case, lemon or onion particles through air) is called *diffusion*. While all particles have the same kinetic energy (KE) at a given temperature, not all particles diffuse at the same rate. Heavier particles move more slowly than lighter particles.

$$\text{KE} = \frac{1}{2}\ mv^2$$

where *m* equals mass and *v* equals velocity.

Graham's law states that if two gases are under the same temperature and pressure, the rates of diffusion of those gases will be inversely proportional to the square root of the ratio of their masses.

$$\frac{v_1}{v_2} = \sqrt{\frac{m_2}{m_1}}$$

In this lab, you will observe a reaction between two gases and use inverse relations to determine the relationship between molecular mass and rate of diffusion.

Objectives

- Measure the distances two gases move.
- Use inverse relations to calculate the masses and velocities of two gases.
- Compare the two ratios.

Materials

- goggles
- apron
- clear plastic straws (2)
- one-hole rubber stoppers (2)
- metric ruler (1)
- scissors

- tightly stoppered test tube with HCl solution
- tightly stoppered test tube with NH_3 solution
- double-ended cotton swab (1)
- 250-mL beaker (1)
- clear tape

Procedure

1. Be sure to wear safety goggles and a lab apron during this experiment. **Caution: Concentrated HCl and NH_3 burn the skin and damage clothing. NH_3 turns the skin black. Handle both liquids with care. If spills occur, notify your teacher immediately.**

2. Cut one straw and push it into the other as shown at the right. Cover the joint of the straws with clear tape.

3. Fill a 250-mL beaker half full with tap water.

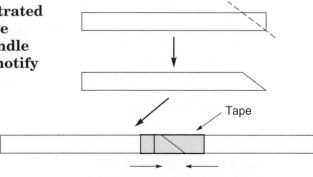

Cut

Tape

Join by pushing together. Then tape.

LAB 26 Rates of Diffusion of Gases

Student Worksheet (continued)

4. Cut a double-ended cotton swab in half and mount each half in a one-hole rubber stopper as shown at the right. Make sure both swabs extend the same length from the stoppers.

5. Attach the joined straws to the lab table with two pieces of clear tape. Label one end HCl and the other end NH_3.

6. Remove the stoppers from test tubes. Replace the solid stoppers with the one-hole stoppers holding the swabs.

7. Gently swirl the tubes to wet the tips of the swabs. Be careful not to wet the stoppers. Remove stoppers with swabs from the test tubes and replace them with the solid stoppers.

8. Hold the swabs by the stoppers and insert the swabs into opposite ends of the joined straws *at the same time.* Be sure you match each swab with the appropriate label at the end of the straw.

9. Do not disturb the straw or the swabs while the reaction takes place. (It may take 3 to 5 minutes.) When the HCl and NH_3 combine, they react to form a white substance. You will observe a white ring at the point on the straws where the HCl and NH_3 meet.

10. Use a marker to mark the straw at the site of the reaction.

11. Mark the straw to locate the tip of each cotton swab.

12. Remove the swabs from the straw and place them in the beaker of water.

13. Measure the distances from the point of the end of each swab to the mark for the reaction ring. Record these distances in the Data and Observations section.

14. Check with your teacher on the disposal of all materials.

Data and Observations

1. Distance NH_3 moved _____ cm

2. Distance HCl moved _____ cm

3. Molecular mass of NH_3 _____ g/mole

4. Molecular mass of HCl _____ g/mole

Analysis

5. Since both gases moved through the straw in the same amount of time, substitute the distance (d) each gas moves for the velocity of the gas,

$\dfrac{d_1}{d_2} = \sqrt{\dfrac{m_2}{m_1}}$. Calculate the ratio of the rates of diffusion. _____

6. What is the ratio of the mass of HCl and NH_3? Compare your experimental ratio with the ratio of molecular mass. How close is your experimental value?

7. Which molecules had the greater velocity? greater mass?

_____

8. Describe in words how *m* and *d* are in inverse variation.

_____

Determining the Order of a Chemical Reaction

LAB
27

Teaching Suggestions

Objectives
- Measure the effect of a reactant concentration on the reaction rate.
- Calculate the natural logarithms and inverses of a reactant's concentration.
- Graph data for one reactant and use them to deduce the reaction order.

Recommended Time   2 class periods

Materials
- 0.15M $Na_2S_2O_3$ (Dissolve 37.2 g of $Na_2S_2O_3 \cdot 5H_2O$ in enough water to give 1 L of solution.)
- 6M HCl (Add 500 mL of concentrated HCl to 400 mL of distilled water and then dilute to give 1 L of solution.)
- aprons (30)
- goggles (30)
- 96-well microplates (15)
- microtip pipets (45)
- distilled water
- white paper
- clock or watch with second hand, or stopwatch
- paper towels
- solid $NaHCO_3$

Teaching the Lab
- **Caution students to be very careful when handling HCl—it is extremely corrosive! Do not allow the solution to come into contact with skin or clothing. If contact does occur, rinse with plenty of water. If the acid contacts skin, apply solid $NaHCO_3$ to neutralize the acid.**
- Before proceeding, be sure students have read and understood the purpose, procedure, and safety precautions for this laboratory activity.
- Have students work in pairs. The lab should take 2 class periods, but students will likely need additional time to complete the calculations and graphs.
- One or more of the lower concentrations of thiosulfate solution in Part 1 (wells A1 through A3) may be skipped to save time. The reactions in these wells often take 10–12 minutes to show obliteration of the x.
- Remind students to remove the reacted solutions from the wells immediately after the reaction has been timed. Remind them not to wait until the entire experiment has been completed to remove the used reaction mixtures. If they wait, it will be impossible to get the reaction mixture out of the microplate.
- Collect pipets students have used to withdraw liquid from each well. Dispose of chemicals in accordance with local, state, and federal regulations.

Lab 27

Determining the Order of a Chemical Reaction

Teaching Suggestions *(continued)*

Data and Observations From Table 1

$S_2O_3^{2-}$ drops	Time (s)	ln ($S_2O_3^{2-}$ drops)	$\dfrac{1}{(S_2O_3^{2-}\ \text{drops})}$
2	240	0.69	0.50
3	180	1.1	0.33
4	120	1.4	0.25
5	95	1.6	0.20
6	75	1.8	0.17
7	58	2.0	0.14
8	42	2.1	0.13
9	36	2.2	0.11
10	30	2.3	0.10
11	24	2.4	0.091
12	22	2.5	0.083

Analysis

13. a.

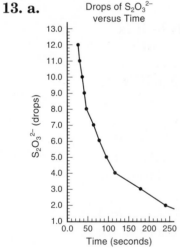

b.

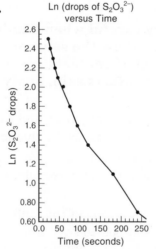

c.

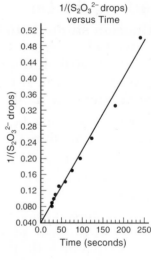

14. a. For the $S_2O_3^{2-}$ solution, the graph of $\dfrac{1}{(\text{drops of } S_2O_3^{2-})}$ versus time gave the best straight line.

   b. second order

Further Explorations

Sulfur forms gradually, and noting the time of its first appearance or when it stops forming would be difficult. However, observing when the "x" disappears provides a point that can be compared in the course of each reaction. Determine the relative rates of the reactions by comparing the times needed to reach the point when the "x" disappears.

LAB 27

Determining the Order of a Chemical Reaction

Student Worksheet

Introduction

In most cases, the concentrations of the reactants in a chemical reaction affect how quickly the reaction takes place. The following expression describes the reaction rate in many reactions:

$$\text{reaction rate} = K(A)^m(B)^n$$
$$= K(\text{concentration of A})^m(\text{concentration of B})^n$$

The order of the reaction, indicated by the exponents m and n, describes how the concentration of each reactant affects the rate. The only way to determine the order of a reaction is to experiment. Each reactant must be tested separately. In this lab, you will test just one reactant in the following reaction:

$$S_2O_2{}^{2-}{}_{(aq)} + 2H^+{}_{(aq)} \rightarrow S_{(cr)} + SO_{2(g)} + H_2O_{(l)}$$

You will vary the concentration of $S_2O_3{}^{2-}$ and keep the concentration of H+ constant. Then you will calculate natural logarithms and inverses of the concentrations of S_2O_3 against the time it takes for the reaction to occur. You will graph your data and use the shape of the graph to determine the order of the reaction with respect to $S_2O_3{}^{2-}$.

Objectives

• Measure the effect of a reactant concentration on the reaction rate.
• Calculate the natural logarithms and inverses of a reactant's concentration.
• Graph data for one reactant and use them to deduce the reaction order.

Materials

• apron
• goggles
• 96-well microplate
• microtip pipets (3)
• distilled water
• white paper
• clock or watch with second hand, or stopwatch
• paper towel
• 0.15M $Na_2S_2O_3$
• 6M HCl

Procedure

Caution: HCl is extremely corrosive. Wear goggles and an apron while completing this laboratory. Do not allow this solution to come into contact with your skin or clothing. If contact does occur, rinse the affected area with plenty of water. If the acid comes into contact with skin, apply solid $NaHCO_3$ to neutralize the acid.

LAB 27 Determining the Order of a Chemical Reaction

Student Worksheet (continued)

1. Arrange your microplate so that the lettered rows are to the left and the numbered columns are at the top. A series of increasingly more concentrated $S_2O_3^{2-}$ solutions will be prepared in row A. Wells in row B will contain a constant concentration of H^+.

2. Add 1 drop of $S_2O_3^{2-}$ to well A1. Add 2 drops of $S_2O_3^{2-}$ solution to well A2. Continue to add $S_2O_3^{2-}$ solution to the wells in row A, increasing the amount added to each well by 1 drop, until you've added 12 drops to well A12.

3. Add 11 drops of distilled water to well A1. Continue to add distilled water to the wells in row A, decreasing the amount added to each well by 1 drop, until you've added 1 drop of distilled water to well A11. *Do not add water to well A12.*

4. Add 5 drops of HCl solution to each well in row B (wells B1 through B12).

5. Write a small "x" on a sheet of white paper. Place well A12 over the "x." Be prepared to observe the well over the "x" and start timing the reaction in seconds the moment the solution from row B is added.

6. Draw up in a microtip pipet all of the solution in well B12. Add the solution from well B12 to well A12. Start timing immediately but go on to step 7.

7. To thoroughly mix the two solutions, draw up the mixture in well A12 and immediately return it to well A12.

8. Observe the mixture in well A12 from above. When the "x" is no longer visible through the liquid, stop timing and record the time elapsed in Table 1 in the Data and Observations section.

9. Withdraw all the liquid from well A12 in a pipet and give the pipet to your teacher to discard. Empty the well immediately, or clean-up will be impossible. Rinse well A12 with distilled water from the pipet and discard the rinse water in the same way that you discarded the first solution.

10. Repeat steps 6 through 9 for each pair of wells A11–B11 through A1–B1. Be sure to place the well with the reacting solutions directly over the "x."

11. Rinse the microplate with distilled water and dry it with a paper towel.

Science and Mathematics Lab Manual

NAME ______________________ DATE __________ PERIOD _____

LAB 27

Determining the Order of a Chemical Reaction

Student Worksheet *(continued)*

Data and Observations

Table 1

Varying $S_2O_3^{2-}$ with Constant H^+												
Well Number:	A1	A2	A3	A4	A5	A6	A7	A8	A9	A10	A11	A12
$S_2O_3^{2-}$ drops												
Time (seconds)												

Analysis

12. Set up and complete Table 2, which should look like the example but have 12 rows. (For purposes of this experiment, take all data to two significant digits.)

Table 2

		Data from Table 1	
$S_2O_3^{2-}$ drops	Time (s)	ln ($S_2O_3^{2-}$ drops)	$\frac{1}{S_2O_3^{2-}\text{ drops}}$
1			
2			

13. Prepare the following graphs and draw the best-fitting line for each.

a. Plot time in seconds on the x-axis and drops of $S_2O_3^{2-}$ solution on the y-axis.

b. Plot time in seconds on the x-axis and the natural logarithm of drops of $S_2O_3^{2-}$ solution on the y-axis.

c. Plot time in seconds on the x-axis and $\frac{1}{\text{drops of } S_2O_3^{2-}}$ on the y-axis.

Lab 27

LAB 27 Determining the Order of a Chemical Reaction

Student Worksheet (continued)

14. Use the table below to deduce the order of the reaction for $S_2O_3^{2-}$.

Straight-line Graph	Order
Drops vs. time	Zero order
Natural log drops vs. time	First order
1/drops vs. time	Second order

a. Which of the three graphs for the $S_2O_3^{2-}$ solution provided the best straight line as its best-fit line?

_____

b. What is the order of the reaction with respect to $S_2O_3^{2-}$?

_____

Measuring Densities of Pennies

Teaching Suggestions

Objectives

- Use arithmetic series to predict the densities of groups of pennies.
- Determine the densities of pennies minted before 1982.
- Compare the densities of pennies minted before 1982 and after 1982.

Recommended Time

- 1 class period

Materials

- 40 pre-1982 pennies (400)
- balances (10)
- 50-mL graduated cylinders (10)
- paper towels (various amount available for drying and spills)
- 20 colored pencils (2 different colors per group)

Preparation

- Have students work in groups of three.
- The zinc-core penny was minted for the first time in 1982, but not all pennies of that year had the new composition. To ensure that all the more recent coins have the zinc core, avoid using 1982 and 1983 coins.
- If you are unable to find 40 pre-1982 pennies for each group, you might want to make up sets with fewer pennies or have groups exchange coins.

Teaching the Lab

- Masses of pennies will vary. Students should not evaluate density on the basis of one determination of mass and one determination of volume.
- Volume should be measured with the smallest graduated cylinder that has an internal diameter great enough to allow free passage of the coins.
- If necessary, remind students that the value they obtain for the slope of each graph line is equivalent to the value for density.

$$\left(\text{Density} = \frac{\text{mass}}{\text{volume}} = \text{g/mL}\right)$$

- Inaccuracy in measuring volume is most likely when few coins are used. This is the reason that no fewer than five coins are used at one time. If a graphing program is available, its use in preparing graphs and finding the slope of graph lines will help to minimize the effects of measurement errors.

Lab 28

Data and Observations
Sample tables

Table 1

		Pre-1982 Pennies	
Number of Pennies	Mass (g)	Total Volume in Cylinder (mL)	Net Volume of Pennies (mL)
5	13.5	21.5	1.5
10	31.5	23.5	3.5
15	40.5	24.5	4.5
20	54.1	26.0	6.0
25	68.5	27.5	7.5
30			
35			
40			

Table 2

		Post-1982 Pennies	
Number of Groups	Mass (g)	Total Volume in Cylinder (mL)	Net Volume of Pennies (mL)
0	0	20	0
1	12.4	21.5	1.5
2	25.2	23.0	3.0
3	37.8	24.5	4.5
4	50.4	26.0	6.0
5	63.0	27.5	7.5
6	75.6	29.0	9.0
7	88.2	30.5	10.5
8	100.8	32.0	12.0
Arithmetic Sequence Equation	$a_n = n(12.6)$	$a_n = 20 + n(1.5)$	$a_n = n(1.5)$

Measuring Densities of Pennies

Teaching Suggestions *(continued)*

Analysis

1.–2.

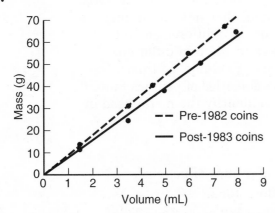

3. Both graphs give a linear relationship between the mass of the pennies and the volume of the pennies. The graphs differ in the slopes of the lines.

4. Answers will vary but the slope of the line for the pre-1982 pennies should approximate the value for the density of copper (8.92 g/mL). Using the sample data, the slope is 9.17. The slope of the line for the post-1982 pennies should approximate the value for the density of zinc (7.14 g/mL). Using the sample data, the slope is 7.83.

5. The values represent the mass of the coins per unit volume (mL), or density.

6. The density of copper is 8.92 g/mL. The slopes students find for this line will vary but should be closer to the density of copper than the slopes they find for the post-1982 coins.

Further Explorations

Archimedes, a Greek mathematician and inventor of the second century b.c., was commissioned by the king of Syracuse to find out whether a crown that had been made for the king was fashioned from pure gold or from a mixture of gold and silver, a less expensive metal. Archimedes could not use chemical tests, for they would damage the crown, yet he was able to find the answer to the king's question. How did he carry out the king's request?

(Knowing that gold is denser than silver, Archimedes reasoned that a given mass of gold would have a smaller volume than would an equal mass of silver or mixture of gold and silver. Suddenly realizing that water displacement is a means of determining volume, Archimedes used this method to compare the volume of the crown with the volume of an equal mass of gold. Because the crown displaced more water than pure gold, Archimedes knew the crown was not pure gold.)

**LAB
28**

Measuring Densities of Pennies

Student Worksheet

Introduction

Today's penny is quite different from the penny of a decade ago. Before 1982, pennies were made of an alloy of copper. Since then, they have been made with an outside coating of copper and an inner core of a different metal. Differences in the composition of the pennies have resulted in different characteristics, including density, or mass per unit of volume. In this experiment, you will determine and compare the densities of pennies minted before and after 1982, and use your data to try to identify the metal used in the core of pennies minted after 1982.

Objectives

• Use arithmetic series to predict the densities of groups of pennies.
• Determine the densities of pennies minted before 1982.
• Compare the densities of pennies minted before 1982 and after 1982.

Materials

• 40 pre-1982 pennies   • balance   • 50-mL graduated cylinder
• paper towels   • 2 different colored pencils

Procedure

A. Mass

1. Find the mass of 5 pennies. Record the mass in Table 1 in the Data and Observations Section

2. Add 5 more pennies to the first group and obtain the mass of these 10 pennies. Record the mass.

3. Repeat step 2, each time adding 5 more pennies to those already on the balance, until you have used all 40 pennies.

B. Volume

4. Fill a 50-mL graduated cylinder to the 20-mL mark with water. Be sure to use the bottom of the meniscus to measure the water level.

5. Still working with the same set of 40 pennies, gently drop 5 of the pennies into the graduated cylinder. Record the new water level in Column 2 of Table 1.

6. Add 5 more pennies to the graduated cylinder, making a total of 10 pennies. Record the water level in the table.

7. Add 5 more pennies to the cylinder and record the water level.

8. Repeat step 7 until you have added all 40 pennies of the set to the cylinder. Record the volume after each addition.

9. Discard the water. Dry the pennies with a paper towel and either pass them to another group to use or give them to your teacher.

10. Find the net volume of each group of pennies by subtracting 20 mL from the total volume recorded for each group (column 3). Enter the net volume for each group in column 4 of Table 1.

LAB 28 Measuring Densities of Pennies

Student Worksheet *(continued)*

11. Table 2 lists information for post-1982 pennies. The data in columns 2–4 follow an arithmetic sequence. For each column, determine the equation that represents the arithmetic sequence shown. Record the equations at the bottom of Table 2.

12. Using the data in Table 2, predict the mass, total volume, and net volume for 6, 7, and 8 groups of pennies. Record your data in Table 2.

Data and Observations

Table 1

Pre-1982 Pennies			
Number of Pennies	Mass (g)	Total Volume in Cylinder (mL)	Net Volume of Pennies (mL)
5			
10			
15			
20			
25			
30			
35			
40			

Table 2

Post-1982 Pennies			
Number of Groups	Mass (g)	Total Volume in Cylinder (mL)	Net Volume of Pennies (mL)
0	0	20	0
1	12.6	21.5	1.5
2	25.2	23.0	3.0
3	37.8	24.5	4.5
4	50.4	26.0	6.0
5	63.0	27.5	7.5
6			
7			
8			
Arithmetic Sequence Equation			

Measuring Densities of Pennies

LAB 28

Student Worksheet *(continued)*

Analysis

1. Construct a graph of your results. Using a colored pencil, plot the data for the pre-1982 pennies first. Let the *y*-axis reflect the mass of the pennies. Plot the net volume of the pennies on the *x*-axis. Then draw the best-fitting straight line (the straight line that connects as many points as possible).

2. On the same graph, plot the data for the post-1982 pennies using a different colored pencil. Draw the best-fitting straight line.

3. How do the graphs compare? Describe their similarities and differences.

   _____

   _____

   _____

4. Find the slope of each line.

   Slope: pre-1982 pennies _____

   Slope: post-1982 pennies _____

5. What do the slope values represent? _____

6. The density of copper is 8.92 g/mL. How does this value compare with the slope of the line for the pre-1982 pennies?

   _____

The Law of Probability

Teaching Suggestions

Objectives
- Use a spinner to determine direction and distance of a movement.
- Use the law of probability to analyze the random movements described by the spinner.

Recommended Time
- 1 class period (Students may need additional time to complete the questions in the Analysis section.)

Materials
- cardboard (10)
- scissors (10 pairs)
- glue or paste
- grid paper (90 sheets)
- metric rulers (10)
- colored pencils (30 total, 3 different colors)
- shirt buttons (10)
- straight pins (10)

Preparation
- Gather materials.

Teaching the Lab
- Have students work in groups of three, with each student doing one trial.
- Students will need to define a successful outcome in order to use the formulas.
- If cardboard is unavailable, the styrofoam flat trays used in cafeterias may be substituted. If straight pins are unavailable, substitute unfolded paper clips.

Data and Observations

Sample Table 1

Turns	Trial 1		Trial 2		Trial 3	
	Direction	Spaces	Direction	Spaces	Direction	Spaces
1	N	2	N	1	SE	6
2	SE	3	S	6	SE	6
3	N	4	E	2	S	5
4	S	2	W	1	E	4
5	SW	5	NW	3	N	3
6	W	6	SE	3	NW	1
7	E	2	NE	5	NW	1
8	SE	1	SW	5	NE	4
9	SE	1	SW	5	SW	5
10	NW	4	NE	2	W	2
11	W	5	SE	4	S	2
12	NE	6	NW	3	E	6
13	E	2	W	6	N	6
14	W	3	E	1	SE	1
15	N	1	S	1	SW	4
16	NW	5	N	6	NE	3
17	NE	4	N	3	NW	2
18	E	4	S	4	W	
19	SE	5	E	2	N	5
20	S	6	W	5	E	3

The Law of Probability

Teaching Suggestions *(continued)*

Sample Graph

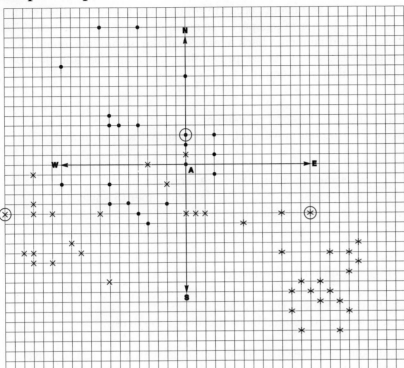

Sample Table 2

Trial 1		Trial 2		Trial 3	
Direction	Distance	Direction	Distance	Direc	Distance
S	2	SW	16	S	13

Average distance:

Group _____

Class _____

Analysis

13. It would be difficult to make an accurate prediction usin data from only three trials.

14. number of favorable outcomes = 1

number of possible outcomes = 48 (6 distances × 8 direc ons)

$$P = \frac{1}{48}$$

Further Explorations

Have students calculate the average distances traveled by the other groups in the class and compare the class average to the group average.

LAB 29

The Law of Probability

Student Worksheet

Introduction

Are there surprises in nature? While many natural events occur in predictable patterns, other events or behaviors are less predictable. Take the behavior of gas particles as an example. Gas particles move haphazardly, bumping into obstacles and bouncing back again. To make predictions about events such as the movements of gas particles, scientists use probability. Use a spinner and the law of probability to make predictions about random movement.

Objectives

- Use a spinner to determine direction and distance of a movement.
- Use the law of probability to analyze the random movements described by the spinner.

Materials

- cardboard (1)
- colored pencils (3 different colors)
- glue or paste
- metric ruler (1)
- scissors
- shirt button (1)
- straight pin (1)
- grid paper (3 sheets)

Procedure

A. Making the Spinner

1. Paste the spinner and pointer in Figure 1 onto the cardboard.
2. Cut out the spinner and pointer.
3. Push the straight pin up through the center dot of the spinner.
4. Place the button on the pin and push the pin through the center dot of the arrow.

B. Spinner

5. Spin the arrow. When it stops, read from the outer dial the direction in which you are to move. Record the direction in Table 1 in the Data and Observations section.
6. Spin the arrow again. When it stops, read from the inner dial the number of spaces you are to move. Record the number of spaces in Table 1. This is Trial 1, Turn 1.
7. Record a total of 20 turns (two spins each turn) for Trial 1.

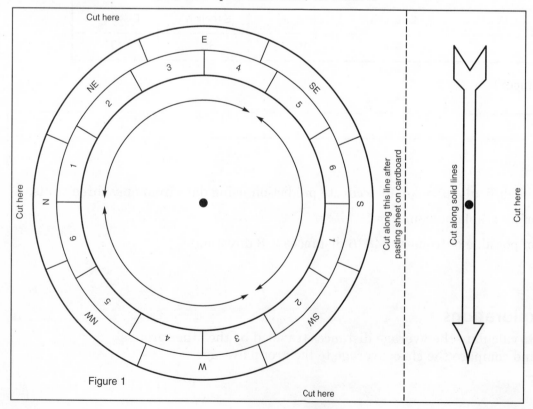

Figure 1

The Law of Probability

Student Worksheet (continued)

8. Spin twenty turns for each of Trials 2 and 3.
9. Start at Point A at the center of Graph 1 and plot your movement for Trial 1, Turn 1. (Draw diagonally if the direction is northeast, southeast, northwest, or southwest. Draw along a grid line if the direction is north, south, east, or west.) From this point, plot your movement for Trial 1, Turn 2. Continue this process for all 20 turns.
10. Using different-colored pencils, plot your movements for Trials 2 and 3. Begin plotting each trial at Point A.
11. Measure the net distances along the straight lines drawn from Point A to the ends of each of your random paths. Record your distances in Table 2.
12. Calculate the average of the distances measured by your group. Record this average in the Data and Observations section.

Data and Observations

Table 1

Turns	Trial 1		Trial 2		Trial 3	
	Direction	Spaces	Direction	Spaces	Direction	Spaces
1						
2						
3						
4						
5						
6						
7						
8						
9						
10						
11						
12						
13						
14						
15						
16						
17						
18						
19						
20						

The Law of Probability

Student Worksheet   *(continued)*

Graph 1

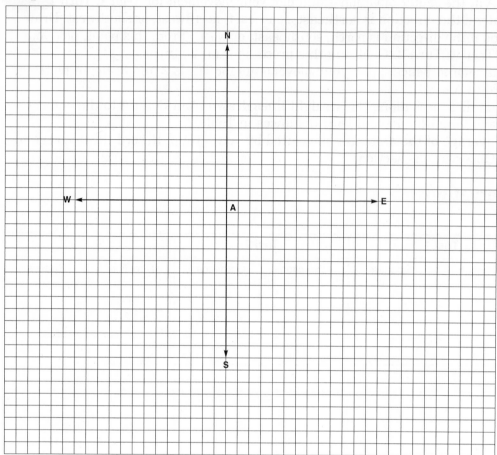

Table 2

Trial 1		Trial 2		Trial 3	
Direction	Distance	Direction	Distance	Direction	Distance

Average distance:

Group _____

Class _____

Analysis

13. Based on your three trials, what prediction can you make about the distance and direction of future paths? How accurate do you think your prediction would be?

_____

14. Use the definition of probability to find the probability of traveling a particular distance and direction in one turn (two spins).

Energy Changes

Teaching Suggestions

Objectives
- Observe the characteristic spectra of sodium.
- Use trigonometric equations to calculate the wavelength of light emitted by sodium.

Recommended Time
- 1 class period

Materials
- aprons (30)
- goggles (30)
- laboratory burners (10)
- diffraction gratings (10)
- metersticks (20)
- cardboard with slit (10)
- slide mounts (optional)
- white paper (10)
- tape (10)
- modeling clay (10)
- commercial preparation of anhydrous carbonate of sodium

Preparation
- Have students work in groups of three.
- Supply the salt in small plastic bottles with lids.
- Dry powdered salt is necessary so that the dust from the salt is drawn up into the burner flame.
- If the salt is prepared several days before use, cover it tightly with plastic. A bag of silica gel will keep the salts dry.

Teaching the Lab
- **Caution: Students should wear goggles and aprons for this laboratory. Students with long hair should tie their hair back. Sodium carbonate can irritate the skin. Use care when handling.**
- The value of n, the number of lines per cm, is different for each type of diffraction grating. The correct value for n should be written on the chalkboard for students to use in their calculations.
- Darken the room to prevent extraneous light from interfering with student observations.
- Especially at the beginning of the experiment, circulate to make sure students have set up the equipment correctly and are using proper techniques for measuring distance of the spectral lines from the flame. This distance is the basis for determining the wavelength.

Data and Observations

Sample table

Spectral Line			
	Color	Distance D	Distance S
Sodium	yellow	33 cm	100 cm

Analysis

1. $H = \sqrt{D^2 + S^2} = 105.3$ cm

2. $\sin \theta = \dfrac{33 \text{ cm}}{105.3} = 0.313$

3. Wavelengths of light were calculated using 5276 lines per cm.

$d = \dfrac{1}{5276} = 1.9 \times 10^{-4}$ cm

4. $\mathring{A} = d \times \sin \theta = 1.9 \times 10^{-4}$ cm $\times\ 0.313$

   $= 1.9 \times 10^{-4}$ cm $\times\ 3.13 \times 10^{-1}$

   $= 5.947 \times 10^{-5}$ cm

   $= 595$ nm (Students will find somewhat different values for the
   wavelength, since these values depend upon the location
   of the spectral lines the students observed.)

Measuring Electron Energy Changes

Student Worksheet

Introduction

Just as each element in the universe has a unique boiling point, so also each element has a unique emission spectra. When the electrons in an element absorb energy, they move to higher energy orbitals. When electrons in these higher energy levels move back to lower energy levels, they emit energy in the form of light. Scientists can determine the identity of a particular element by measuring the wavelength of the light emitted during a flame test. The color of that light is an important clue to the identity of the element.

In this laboratory activity, you will work with two partners to observe the color and location of the spectral lines of sodium. Using trigonometric equations and other formulas, you will determine its wavelength.

Objectives

* Observe the characteristic spectra of sodium.
* Use trigonometric equations to calculate the wavelength of light emitted by sodium

Materials

* apron
* laboratory burner
* meterstick (2)
* slide mount (optional)
* tape
* modeling clay

* goggles
* diffraction grating
* cardboard with slit
* white paper
* sample of anhydrous sodium carbona   salts

Procedure

Caution: Wear goggles and aprons. Tie back long hair.

A. Spectrometer (see diagram)

1. Fasten a meter stick to the table using modeling clay. Atta   a piece of cardboard with a slit using clay so that the slit is directly line with the center of the meterstick.

2. From the center of the meterstick, position another meterstick perpendicularly and attach it to the table with clay. Place a diffraction grating, mounted on a card or slide mount, at a distance of 100 cm from the slit. (This is distance *S*.)

3. Place a laboratory burner behind the cardboard. Be sure the cardboard will not be too close to the flame.

4. Tape a sheet of paper on the wall behind the burner on one side of the slit. Light the burner and adjust the flame until it is totally blue. Check to be certain that you can observe the flame through the slit.

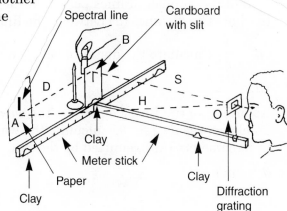

LAB 30

Measuring Electron Energy Changes

Student Worksheet (continued)

B. Spectral Line Observation

5. Obtain a covered bottle of sodium carbonate.

6. You and your partners will need to work together to collect the data.
   A. Student A looks through the diffraction grating.
   B. Student B will mark the paper where student A sees a spectral line appearing.
   C. Student C will supply the flame with powdered salt.

7. Student A observes the burner flame through the diffraction grating and slit. Student C shakes a covered bottle of salt and then opens it close to the collar (air inlet) of the burner. Student B marks the location of a spectral line on the paper on the wall. Note the color of the spectral line that Student A observes in the table in the Data and Observations section.

8. Measure the distance from the slit to the sighted spectral line. Record this distance (D) in the table in the Data and Observations section.

Data and Observations

Spectral Line			
	Color	Distance D	Distance S
Sodium			

Analysis

1. Use the Pythagorean Theorem to determine the distance (H) from the diffraction grating directly to the spectral line.

   $H = \sqrt{D^2 + S^2}$ = _____

2. The sine of angle AOB of triangle AOB is $\sin \theta = \dfrac{D}{H}$. Find the value of $\sin \theta$.

   $\sin \theta =$ _____

3. Obtain the number of lines per cm in the diffraction grating (n) from your teacher. The distance (d) between the lines in the spectral line is

   $d = \dfrac{1}{n}$. Calculate the distance between the lines in the spectral line.

   $d =$ _____

4. According to the Bragg equation, the wavelength of light (A) emitted by an element is $d \times \sin \theta$. Calculate the wavelength of the light, measured in nanometers (nm), emitted by the salt.

   $d \times \sin \theta =$ _____

Appendix: TI-83 Programs

Program: HEAT

```
{6,Ø}→L₁:Send(L₁)
1→Xmin:2→Xmax:1→Ymin:2→Ymax
GridOff
AxesOff
LabelOff
PlotsOff
FnOff
ClrDraw
Text(1,16,"TEXAS  INSTRUMENTS")
Text(8,3Ø,"CBL  SYSTEM")
Text(15,1Ø,"EXPERIMENT  WORKBOOK")
Text(29,32,"HEAT  V2.Ø")
Text(36,18,"(EXPERIMENT
M5)")
Text(5Ø,6,"PRESS  [ENTER]  ON  TI-83"
Pause
ClrHome
Disp "TURN ON THE CBL."
Output(4,1Ø,"[ENTER]")
Pause
Full
ClrHome
Disp "NOW CHECKING THE"
Disp "CALCULATOR-CBL"
Disp "LINK CONNECTION."
Disp "PLEASE WAIT...."
{1,0}→L₁
Send(L₁)
{Ø}→L₂
Lbl M
{7}→L₁
Send(L₁)
Get(L₂)
If dim(L₂)=1 and L₂(1)=Ø
Then
ClrHome
Disp "***LINK ERROR***"
Disp "PUSH IN THE LINK"
Disp "CORD CONNECTORS"
Disp "FIRMLY THEN HIT"
Disp "[ENTER]."
Pause
Goto M
End
Disp ""
Output(6,1," STATUS: O.K."
Output(8,1Ø,"[ENTER]")
Pause
Func
ClrHome
ClrDraw
```

```
AxesOn
ClrDraw
ClrList L₃,L₄
−1Ø→Ymin
9Ø→Ymax
1Ø→Yscl
{6,0}→L₁
Send(L₁)
{1,Ø}→L₁
Send(L₁)
{1,1,1}→L₁
Send(L₁)
36→dim(L₃
36→dim(L₄
Lbl L
ClrHome
Disp "HOW MUCH TIME"
Disp "BETWEEN POINTS"
Disp "IN SECONDS?"
Input T
If T ≤ Ø:Goto L
−2*T→Xmin
36*T→Xmax
T→Xscl
seq(I,I,T,36*T,T)→L₃
ClrHome
Disp "PRESS ENTER"
Disp "TO START"
Pause
ClrHome
{3Ø−1,Ø}→L₁
Send(L₁)
For(I,1,36,1)
Get(L₄(I))
Pt-On(L₃(I),L₄(I))
End
ClrHome
Plot1(Scatter,L₃,L₄, · )
DispGraph
Stop
```

Appendix: TI-83 Programs

Program: HIKER

```
{6,Ø}→L₁:Send(L₁)
1→Xmin:2→Xmax:1→Ymin:2→Ymax
GridOff
AxesOff
LabelOff
PlotsOff
FnOff
ClrDraw
Text(1,16,"TEXAS  INSTRUMENTS")
Text(8,3Ø,"CBL  SYSTEM")
Text(15,1Ø,"EXPERIMENT  WORKBOOK")
Text(29,3Ø,"HIKER  V2.Ø")
Text(36,18,"(EXPERIMENT  M1)")
Text(5Ø,6,"PRESS  [ENTER]  ON  TI-83"
Pause
ClrHome
Disp "TURN ON THE CBL."
Output(4,1Ø,"[ENTER]")
Pause
Full
ClrHome
Disp "NOW CHECKING THE"
Disp "CALCULATOR-CBL"
Disp "LINK CONNECTION."
Disp "PLEASE WAIT...."
{1,Ø}→L₁
Send(L₁)
{Ø}→L₂
Lbl M
{7}→L₁
Send(L₁)
Get(L₂)
If dim(L₂)= 1 and L₂(1)=Ø
Then
ClrHome
Disp "***LINK ERROR***"
Disp "PUSH IN THE LINK"
Disp "CORD CONNECTORS"
Disp "FIRMLY THEN HIT"
Disp "[ENTER]."
Pause
Goto M
End
Disp ""
Output(6,1," STATUS: O.K."
Output(8,1Ø,"[ENTER]")
Pause
Func
ClrHome
ClrDraw
```

```
AxesOn
ClrList L₂,L₃
Ø→Xmin
6→Xmax
.1→Xscl
Ø→Ymin
2Ø→Ymax
1→Yscl
6Ø→dim(L₂
6Ø→dim(L₃
seq(I,I,.1,6,.1)→L₂
{6,Ø}→L₁
Send(L₁)
{1,Ø}L₁
:Send(L₁)
{1,11,3}→L₁
Send(L₁)
ClrHome
Disp "PRESS ENTER"
Disp "TO START"
Disp "GRAPH"
Pause
ClrDraw
Text(4,1,"DIST(FT)")
Text(51,78,"TIME(S)")
{3,.1,−1,Ø}→L₁
Send(L₁)
For(I,1,6Ø,1)
Get(L₃(I))
Pt-On(L₂(I),L₃(I))
End
{6,Ø}→L₁
:Send(L₁)
Plot1(Scatter,L₂,L₃,·)
Text(4,1,"DIST(FT)")
Text(51,78,"TIME(S)")
Stop
```

Appendix: TI-83 Programs

PROGRAM:PH

```
{6,Ø}→L1:Send(L1)
1→Xmin:2→Xmax:1→Ymin:2→Ymax
GridOff
AxesOff
LabelOff
PlotsOff
FnOff
ClrDraw
Text(1,16,"TEXAS  INSTRUMENTS")
Text(8,3Ø,"CBL  SYSTEM")
Text(15,1Ø,"EXPERIMENT  WORKBOOK")
Text(29,36,"PH  V2.Ø")
Text(36,3,"(EXPERIMENT  C1,C2,C4,C5)")
Text(5Ø,6,"PRESS  [ENTER]  ON  TI-83"
Pause
ClrHome
Disp "TURN ON THE CBL."
Output(4,1Ø,"[ENTER]")
Pause
```

```
AxesOn
−5→Xmin
5Ø→Xmax
5→Xscl
−2→Ymin
14→Ymax
1→Yscl
ClrList L4,L5
ClrHome
{6,Ø}→L1
Send(L1)
{1,Ø}→L1
Send(L1)
{4,1,1,1,13.662,−3.8Ø7}→L1
Send(L1)
{1,1,1,Ø,Ø,1}→L1
Send(L1)
ClrDraw
Lbl L
ClrHome
```

```
Disp "NOW CHECKING THE"
Disp "CALCULATOR-CBL"
Disp "LINK CONNECTION."
Disp "PLEASE WAIT...."
{1,Ø}→L1
Send(L1)
{Ø}→L2
Lbl M
{7}→L1
Send(L1)
Get(L2)
If dim(L2)=1 and L2(1)=Ø
Then
ClrHome
Disp "***LINK ERROR***"
Disp "PUSH IN THE LINK"
Disp "CORD CONNECTORS"
Disp "FIRMLY THEN HIT"
Disp "[ENTER]."
Pause
Goto M
End
Disp ""
Output(6,1," STATUS: O.K."
Output(8,1Ø,"[ENTER]")
Pause
Func
ClrHome
ClrDraw
```

```
Input C
If C < 1 or C ≠ int(C):Goto L
C→dim(L4
ClrHome
{3,Ø,−1,6}→L1
Send(L1)
Disp "PLEASE ALLOW"
Disp "SYSTEM 3Ø"
Disp "SECONDS TO"
Disp "WARM UP"
Output(6,1Ø,"[ENTER]")
Pause
ClrHome
Disp "PRESS TRIGGER"
Disp "TO COLLECT"
Disp "PH READINGS"
For(I,1,C,1)
Get(L4(I))
Disp "ML?"
Input D
D→L5(I)
Pt-On(L5(I),L4(I))
End
max(L5)→Xmax
(−.1)*Xmax→Xmin
Plot1(xyLine,L5,L4·)
Text(7,1,"P")
Text(14,1,"H")
Text(55,78,"ML")
```

Appendix: TI-83 Programs

PROGRAM:TEMP
```
{6,Ø}→L₁:Send(L₁)
1→Xmin:2→Xmax:1→Ymin:2→Ymax
GridOff
AxesOff
LabelOff
PlotsOff
FnOff
ClrDraw
Text(1,16,"TEXAS  INSTRUMENTS")
Text(8,3Ø,"CBL  SYSTEM")
Text(15,1Ø,"EXPERIMENT  WORKBOOK")
Text(29,32,"TEMP  V2.Ø")
Text(36,18,"(EXPERIMENT  C7)")
Text(5Ø,6,"PRESS  [ENTER]  ON  TI-83"
Pause
ClrHome
Disp "TURN ON THE CBL."
Output(4,1Ø,"[ENTER]")
Pause
Full
ClrHome
Disp "NOW CHECKING THE"
Disp "CALCULATOR-CBL"
Disp "LINK CONNECTION."
Disp "PLEASE WAIT...."
{1,Ø}→L₁
Send(L₁)
{Ø}→L₂
Lbl M
{7}→L₁
Send(L₁)
Get(L₂)
If dim(L₂)=1 and L₂(1)=Ø
Then
ClrHome
Disp "***LINK ERROR***"
Disp "PUSH IN THE LINK"
Disp "CORD CONNECTORS"
Disp "FIRMLY THEN HIT"
Disp "[ENTER]."
Pause
Goto M
End
Disp ""
Output(6,1," STATUS: O.K."
Output(8,1Ø,"[ENTER]")
Pause
Func
ClrHome
ClrDraw
```

```
AxesOn
Ø→Xmin
99→Xmax
1Ø→Xscl
Ø→Ymin
9Ø→Ymax
1Ø→Yscl
ClrList L₄,L₅
ClrHome
{6,Ø}→L₁
Send(L₁)
{1,Ø}→L₁
Send(L₁)
{1,1,1}→L₁
Send(L₁)
Lbl L
ClrHome
Disp "ENTER NUMBER"
Disp "OF SAMPLES"
Input C
If C < 1 or C ≠ int(C):Goto L
C→dim(L₄
ClrHome
Disp "PRESS ENTER TO"
Disp "START"
Disp "TEMPERATURE"
Disp "GRAPH"
Pause
ClrDraw
{3,4,−1,Ø}→L₁
Send(L₁)
For(I,1,C,1)
Get(L₄(I))
Pt-On(I,L₄(I))
End
C→dim(L₅
seq(I,I,Ø,C*4-1,4)→L₅
Plot1(xyLine,L₅,L₄·)
ZoomStat
```